TOTAL FOCUS®

By Dr. Robert Myers, Child Psychologist

A Comprehensive Program to Improve Attention,
Concentration and Self-Control in Children

Legacy Publishing Company
10 Speirs Street
Westbrook, ME 04092

1-800-460-2235
www.trytotalfocus.com

Dr. Robert Myers, Child Psychologist

Dr. Robert Myers is a clinical psychologist with 25 years of experience working with children, adolescents, families and parents. He has specialized in working with children and adolescents with Attention Deficit Hyperactivity Disorder and learning disabilities. Dr. Myers earned his Ph.D. from the University of Southern California. In addition to his 20 years of private practice, he has also held a number of clinical positions. These have included Clinical Director for several youth service inpatient units at College Hospital and Charter Hospital of Long Beach; Consulting Psychologist for Miller Children's Hospital at Long Beach Memorial Medical Center; Clinical Instructor (Pediatrics), Volunteer Faculty UCI College of Medicine; and Adjunct Professor, Rosemead Graduate School of Psychology at BIOLA University and Alliance International University. He has also provided community lectures on parenting and other topics. Dr. Bob has been a talk show host on KIEV and KORG in Southern California and has also appeared as a guest on many radio and television talk shows locally and nationally. He was also a regular columnist for **Parents** and **Kids Magazine**.

Preface

This project is based on my 25 years of experience working with children and adolescents who have ADHD and learning disabilities. Time and again, I have observed families entering treatment with the parents totally exasperated, and the child frustrated and downhearted. I have learned that it is important for the parent and child to thoroughly understand why the problems they have faced exist. I assure them that the parents did not cause their children to be the way they are. I also assure the children that they are not "stupid" or "bad." Once they understand that the problems result from "faulty wiring" in the brain, and that it can be fixed, they are relieved and ready to work together on turning things around. The most gratifying thing I have experienced over the years is to share in the happiness of parents and children when they are successful. This project is aimed at providing parents much of the information and techniques I have provided to these families in a form that can be used conveniently, affordably and successfully at home by many more families.

My special thanks to my wife, Pam, for all her love, help, understanding, and encouragement during my career, and for her expert advice as a parent and former teacher in developing this project.

I dedicate this project to my own two children, Lauren and Greg. I thank God for their presence in my life and the joy they bring to me and my wife.

Please listen to the Parent's Audio Lesson, _Introduction: One-on-One with Dr. Bob_ before continuing on in the workbook.

Introduction

Welcome to Total Focus. This program is designed to help children learn to improve their attention, concentration, motivation, self-control and self-esteem at school and at home. It is particularly helpful for children with conditions known as Attention Deficit Disorder (ADD) or Attention Deficit Hyperactivity Disorder (ADHD). While developed to serve this population of children, it is helpful for any child who needs to improve in the areas mentioned above. For purposes of discussion and for simplicity in this program, we will refer to the condition as ADHD. We will also use "he," "him" and "his" to refer to children, again for simplicity. Total Focus is designed to work for boys and girls alike.

The Total Focus Program is the product of my years of working with children and adolescents with ADHD and their parents. It may be used if the child is taking medication for ADHD or if he is not.

This program uses a team approach to improving attention, concentration, and self-control. The team consists of the parents, the child, and the child's teacher or teachers. We use a system of behavior modification, biofeedback and relaxation techniques, and cognitive behavior therapy, including cognitive rehabilitation or "brain training" exercises. I have used this system successfully with hundreds of kids with ADHD. It's a simple program that you can do with your child in just minutes a day. The first step is to identify the behaviors that are issues with your child.

On the pages that follow, you will find three copies of the Total Focus Behavior Checklist. Please complete the checklist, giving thought to your child's ability to pay attention and concentrate, the degree of hyperactivity, and behavior and self-control issues. If you live in a two-parent household, it is helpful for both parents to fill out the checklist. I recommend that you ask your child's teacher to fill out the Behavior Checklist as well.

If you have two or more children with ADHD, or you suspect they may have it, more copies of the Behavior Checklist are provided in the Appendix.

 Please complete the Behavior Checklist on the next page.

TOTAL FOCUS Behavior Checklist

For each item, check the column which best describes this child:	Not at All (0)	Just a Little (1)	Quite a Bit (2)	Very Much (3)	Score
1. Often fails to give close attention to details or makes careless mistakes in schoolwork or tasks					
2. Often has difficulty sustaining attention in tasks or play activities					
3. Often does not seem to listen when spoken to directly					
4. Often does not follow through on instructions and fails to finish schoolwork, chores, or duties					
5. Often has difficulty organizing tasks and activities					
6. Often avoids, dislikes, or reluctantly engages in tasks requiring sustained mental effort					
7. Often loses things necessary for activities (e.g., toys, school assignments, pencils, or books)					
8. Often is distracted by outside stimuli					
9. Often is forgetful in daily activities					
10. Often has difficulty maintaining alertness, orienting to requests, or executing directions					
A - TOTAL SCORE (Attention/Concentration)					
11. Often fidgets with hands or feet or squirms in seat					
12. Often leaves seat in classroom or in other situations in which remaining seated is expected					
13. Often runs about or climbs excessively in situations in which remaining seated is expected					
14. Often has difficulty playing or engaging in leisure activities quietly					
15. Often is "on the go" or often acts as if "driven by a motor"					
16. Often talks excessively					
17. Often blurts out answers before questions have been completed					
18. Often has difficulty awaiting turn					
19. Often interrupts or intrudes on others (e.g., butts into conversations/games)					
20. Often has difficulty sitting still, being quiet, or inhibiting impulses in the classroom or at home					
B - TOTAL SCORE (Hyperactivity)					

 Checklist continued on back.

5

TOTAL FOCUS Behavior Checklist

For each item, check the column which best describes this child:	Not at All (0)	Just a Little (1)	Quite a Bit (2)	Very Much (3)	Score
21. Often has trouble taking no for an answer					
22. Often is excitable, impulsive					
23. Often cries easily					
24. Often loses temper					
25. Often blames others for his or her mistakes or misbehavior					
26. Often is restless or overactive					
27. Often disturbs other children					
28. Often changes mood quickly and drastically					
29. Often easily frustrated if demands are not met immediately					
30. Often is negative, defiant, disobedient, or hostile toward authority figures					
C - TOTAL SCORE (Behavior/Self-Control)					
31. Has difficulty getting started on classroom assignments					
32. Has difficulty staying on task for an entire classroom period					
33. Has problems in completion of work on classroom assignments					
34. Has problems in accuracy or neatness of written work in the classroom					
35. Has difficulty attending to a group classroom activity or discussion					
36. Has difficulty making transitions to the next topic or classroom period					
37. Has problems in interactions with peers in the classroom					
38. Has problems in interactions with staff (teacher or aide)					
39. Has difficulty remaining quiet according to classroom rules					
40. Has difficulty staying seated according to classroom rules					
D - TOTAL SCORE (Academic Achievement/School)					
OVERALL TOTAL SCORE (A+B+C+D)					

TOTAL FOCUS **Behavior Checklist**					
For each item, check the column which best describes this child:	Not at All (0)	Just a Little (1)	Quite a Bit (2)	Very Much (3)	Score
1. Often fails to give close attention to details or makes careless mistakes in schoolwork or tasks					
2. Often has difficulty sustaining attention in tasks or play activities					
3. Often does not seem to listen when spoken to directly					
4. Often does not follow through on instructions and fails to finish schoolwork, chores, or duties					
5. Often has difficulty organizing tasks and activities					
6. Often avoids, dislikes, or reluctantly engages in tasks requiring sustained mental effort					
7. Often loses things necessary for activities (e.g., toys, school assignments, pencils, or books)					
8. Often is distracted by outside stimuli					
9. Often is forgetful in daily activities					
10. Often has difficulty maintaining alertness, orienting to requests, or executing directions					
A - TOTAL SCORE (Attention/Concentration)					
11. Often fidgets with hands or feet or squirms in seat					
12. Often leaves seat in classroom or in other situations in which remaining seated is expected					
13. Often runs about or climbs excessively in situations in which remaining seated is expected					
14. Often has difficulty playing or engaging in leisure activities quietly					
15. Often is "on the go" or often acts as if "driven by a motor"					
16. Often talks excessively					
17. Often blurts out answers before questions have been completed					
18. Often has difficulty awaiting turn					
19. Often interrupts or intrudes on others (e.g., butts into conversations/games)					
20. Often has difficulty sitting still, being quiet, or inhibiting impulses in the classroom or at home					
B - TOTAL SCORE (Hyperactivity)					

 Checklist continued on back.

Total Focus Behavior Checklist

For each item, check the column which best describes this child:	Not at All (0)	Just a Little (1)	Quite a Bit (2)	Very Much (3)	Score
21. Often has trouble taking no for an answer					
22. Often is excitable, impulsive					
23. Often cries easily					
24. Often loses temper					
25. Often blames others for his or her mistakes or misbehavior					
26. Often is restless or overactive					
27. Often disturbs other children					
28. Often changes mood quickly and drastically					
29. Often easily frustrated if demands are not met immediately					
30. Often is negative, defiant, disobedient, or hostile toward authority figures					
C - TOTAL SCORE (Behavior/Self-Control)					
31. Has difficulty getting started on classroom assignments					
32. Has difficulty staying on task for an entire classroom period					
33. Has problems in completion of work on classroom assignments					
34. Has problems in accuracy or neatness of written work in the classroom					
35. Has difficulty attending to a group classroom activity or discussion					
36. Has difficulty making transitions to the next topic or classroom period					
37. Has problems in interactions with peers in the classroom					
38. Has problems in interactions with staff (teacher or aide)					
39. Has difficulty remaining quiet according to classroom rules					
40. Has difficulty staying seated according to classroom rules					
D - TOTAL SCORE (Academic Achievement/School)					
OVERALL TOTAL SCORE (A+B+C+D)					

TOTAL FOCUS Behavior Checklist

For each item, check the column which best describes this child:	Not at All (0)	Just a Little (1)	Quite a Bit (2)	Very Much (3)	Score
1. Often fails to give close attention to details or makes careless mistakes in schoolwork or tasks					
2. Often has difficulty sustaining attention in tasks or play activities					
3. Often does not seem to listen when spoken to directly					
4. Often does not follow through on instructions and fails to finish schoolwork, chores, or duties					
5. Often has difficulty organizing tasks and activities					
6. Often avoids, dislikes, or reluctantly engages in tasks requiring sustained mental effort					
7. Often loses things necessary for activities (e.g., toys, school assignments, pencils, or books)					
8. Often is distracted by outside stimuli					
9. Often is forgetful in daily activities					
10. Often has difficulty maintaining alertness, orienting to requests, or executing directions					
A - TOTAL SCORE (Attention/Concentration)					
11. Often fidgets with hands or feet or squirms in seat					
12. Often leaves seat in classroom or in other situations in which remaining seated is expected					
13. Often runs about or climbs excessively in situations in which remaining seated is expected					
14. Often has difficulty playing or engaging in leisure activities quietly					
15. Often is "on the go" or often acts as if "driven by a motor"					
16. Often talks excessively					
17. Often blurts out answers before questions have been completed					
18. Often has difficulty awaiting turn					
19. Often interrupts or intrudes on others (e.g., butts into conversations/games)					
20. Often has difficulty sitting still, being quiet, or inhibiting impulses in the classroom or at home					
B - TOTAL SCORE (Hyperactivity)					

 Checklist continued on back.

TOTAL F●CUS Behavior Checklist

For each item, check the column which best describes this child:	Not at All (0)	Just a Little (1)	Quite a Bit (2)	Very Much (3)	Score
21. Often has trouble taking no for an answer					
22. Often is excitable, impulsive					
23. Often cries easily					
24. Often loses temper					
25. Often blames others for his or her mistakes or misbehavior					
26. Often is restless or overactive					
27. Often disturbs other children					
28. Often changes mood quickly and drastically					
29. Often easily frustrated if demands are not met immediately					
30. Often is negative, defiant, disobedient, or hostile toward authority figures					
C - TOTAL SCORE (Behavior/Self-Control)					
31. Has difficulty getting started on classroom assignments					
32. Has difficulty staying on task for an entire classroom period					
33. Has problems in completion of work on classroom assignments					
34. Has problems in accuracy or neatness of written work in the classroom					
35. Has difficulty attending to a group classroom activity or discussion					
36. Has difficulty making transitions to the next topic or classroom period					
37. Has problems in interactions with peers in the classroom					
38. Has problems in interactions with staff (teacher or aide)					
39. Has difficulty remaining quiet according to classroom rules					
40. Has difficulty staying seated according to classroom rules					
D - TOTAL SCORE (Academic Achievement/School)					
OVERALL TOTAL SCORE (A+B+C+D)					

INTRODUCTION - CONTINUED

Let's take a closer look now at ADHD and the system you'll be using to improve your child's attention, concentration, and self-control.

What is Attention Deficit Hyperactivity Disorder (ADHD)?

ADHD is a medical problem that affects millions of children. These children have at least one of these problems: inattention, impulsivity, and hyperactivity. It seems to be found more frequently in boys than girls (3:1). Some individuals who are diagnosed as having ADHD as children appear to outgrow it as they get older. Most successful adults with ADHD have learned to adapt to it. The Total Focus Program will teach your child how to adapt to the disorder. In some cases, the diagnosis may not even be made until the person is an adolescent or an adult. Individuals with ADHD are usually very bright, creative, sensitive people. Many grow up to become very successful later in life.

What are the symptoms of ADHD?

Inattention:

- often fails to finish what he starts
- doesn't seem to listen
- easily distracted
- has difficulty concentrating or paying attention
- doesn't stick with a play activity

Impulsivity:

- often acts without thinking and later feels sorry
- shifts excessively from one activity to another
- has difficulty organizing work
- needs a lot of supervision
- speaks out loud in class
- doesn't wait to take turns in games or groups

Hyperactivity:

- runs about or climbs on things excessively
- can't sit still and is fidgety
- has difficulty staying in his seat and bothers classmates
- excessive activity during sleep
- always "on the go" and acts as if "driven"

What are the causes of ADHD?

Current research supports the theory that ADHD may be either inherited due to yet unknown genetic factors or that it may be acquired due to environmental factors such as complications of pregnancy, labor or delivery, as well as lead poisoning or head injury. True ADHD is the result of a dysfunction of the brain. A person may have ADHD symptoms, but from another cause such as an emotional disturbance (anxiety or depression) or a medical problem such as allergies, a thyroid disorder, lead poisoning, or the side effects of a medication.

INTRODUCTION

11

The brain functioning of individuals diagnosed with ADHD is significantly different from normal individuals. The areas of the brain where the deficits in brain activity are found to occur are known to be associated with such functions as attention, concentration, planning ahead, and impulse control. Brain function in ADHD individuals has shown a marked improvement when the subjects are on their medication. It is important to note that research related to other brain disorders has shown that cognitive behavioral therapy has been shown to not only improve the psychological symptoms but to improve brain functioning as well. It is quite possible that this may be true for ADHD as well. This would explain why some children are able to show significant improvement with the various psychological methods used in Total Focus.

How is ADHD diagnosed?

Physical Examination and History: One of the first steps should be a complete physical examination by the child's physician to exclude medical causes for the symptoms. Also, the physician will review the child's developmental history as well as medical, school, and social history for clues that will be helpful in making a diagnosis.

Psychological Testing: Questionnaires are used to determine the extent and type of symptoms found in the home and school environment. Testing by a school psychologist or a clinical psychologist can determine if learning disabilities are present that may be causing the symptoms. Behavior analysis tests such as the Total Focus Behavior Checklist may help to discover if a psychological problem may be causing the symptoms. Also, a neuropsychological test such as the Conners CPT to assess brain functioning may be helpful in making the correct diagnosis. No one test or procedure is sufficient for a professional to make a diagnosis.

Team Consultation: Sometimes the child's physician may consult with the parent, school, psychologist, or psychiatrist or other medical specialists such as a neurologist or an allergist in coming to a conclusion on a diagnosis.

How is ADHD treated?

Depending upon the severity of the symptoms, a number of treatment approaches may be used to reduce symptoms and improve behavior.

Medication: This is probably the most often recommended form of treatment, particularly in cases with moderate to severe symptoms. The medications that are most likely to be used are called psychostimulants. They improve brain functioning in the areas that regulate attention and impulse control.

For cases with mild to moderate symptoms, psychoeducational treatment methods may achieve good results in reducing symptoms and improving behavior. Even when it is decided to use medication early in treatment, my experience has been that the psychoeducational methods in the Total Focus Program, combined with medication, may provide the best results.

Behavior Modification: Use of specialized reward systems has proven to provide the motivation and feedback necessary for some children to develop the cognitive strategies needed to improve attention, concentration, task completion, and impulse control. Use of these strategies over time seems to alter brain function and, in some cases, provides long lasting improvement. A slightly different approach at home can also reduce arguing and anger outbursts, along with increasing children's ability to follow directions. We'll be using a behavior modification system in Lesson Two (On Task and In Control at School) and Lesson Four (On Task and In Control at Home).

Relaxation Training and Biofeedback: Learning how to relax can lead to improved self-control as well as improved attention and concentration. Being able to calm down the nervous system at will prevents angry outbursts. Learning to increase general relaxation throughout the day increases alpha waves in the brain, which play a part in learning activities. We'll teach you a number of wonderful biofeedback and relaxation techniques in Lesson Three and throughout the Total Focus Program.

Cognitive Rehabilitation or "Brain Training": Mental exercises are used by patients with brain injuries such as a stroke, or accident victims to retrain their brains so they can get back to their normal activities. Some research shows that children and adults with ADHD can use similar exercises to train their brains to work better at certain tasks, such as attention and simple information processing. In Lessons Five and Six, we'll be using brain training exercises to help your child improve his ability to slow down and think before he does things and to improve attention and concentration.

Cognitive Behavioral Therapy: Recent approaches to psychological counseling emphasize teaching children and adults how to change the way they think about themselves, other people, and their world in general. As they change how they think, they find that it automatically changes how they feel and how they behave. For ADHD children, this technique can lead to improved problem solving, social skills and self-esteem. The Total Focus Program uses cognitive behavioral therapy throughout to help your child change the way he thinks about himself, about people, and the world around him, to achieve better behavior and academic performance.

Parent Education: It is important for parents to understand why their child is having problems at home and/or at school and to learn how to help him to improve his behavior and learning skills. My experience has been that many parents don't have enough information about ADHD to make truly informed decisions about their child's education and treatment. In The Total Focus Program, we'll arm you with the information you need.

Other Methods: Use of special diets has not proven to be effective in treating ADHD. Certainly, eating healthy food is good for all children including those with ADHD. In some children, eating foods with refined sugars and artificial ingredients may make their symptoms worse, but they are not the actual cause of ADHD.

Recently, there have been several new "natural" substances reported to "cure" ADHD. So far, their use has been supported by testimonials from people who claim positive results after using these products. Scientific research has yet to prove whether these substances work any better than sugar pills (which can have up to 50% success with some medical conditions) or are safer than drugs or other treatment methods which have been proven to be successful in clinical trials.

What about children with ADHD and Learning Disabilities?

Some children may have trouble learning because they have difficulty paying attention and concentrating. (These children have ADHD.) Other children may have trouble paying attention and concentrating because they have difficulty processing information. (These children have learning disabilities such as dyslexia). Some children may have both ADHD and learning disabilities. It is important to determine the exact cause of learning problems. Children with learning disabilities usually require Special Education services from the school.

In Focus

- ADHD is a brain disorder that occurs in millions of children. The "wiring" of the brain is different from 95% of the population.

- Children can learn to adapt to ADHD and be very successful in school and in life.

- The Total Focus Program uses a simple, three-step process to help children overcome this difference in wiring and adapt to the disorder: behavior modification, relaxation and biofeedback, and brain training.

- Our overall approach is known as Cognitive Behavioral Therapy. It can be used alone or as a complement to medication.

- We use positive reinforcement and fun for the whole family in lessons that take just minutes a day.

What's Next?

After you have completed the Behavior Checklist and you have read Dr. Bob's introduction, please continue with Lesson One in the workbook. We'll discuss your answers on the Behavior Checklist and how you can use the results to help your child.

Let's Get Focused

HOW TO USE THE BEHAVIOR CHECKLIST TO HELP YOUR CHILD

By now you have filled out the Behavior Checklist. Ideally both parents or the significant adults involved in parenting your child have filled it out, as well as your child's teacher. You can score the checklists simply by adding up the scores in each section and then adding up the total.

What does the total score say about your child? Most likely, the higher the total score, the more the ADHD diagnosis is affecting your child, you, and your family.

Many parents find the scores in sections A and B to be most helpful. If your child's score in Section A is much higher than Section B, then the primary problem is attention and concentration. If Section B is much higher than Section A, then your child's primary problem is in the area of hyperactivity and impulse control. If they are both equally high, then your child has problems in both areas.

This corresponds to the way health professionals currently diagnose ADHD, which is predominately inattentive, predominately hyperactive or mixed.

If your child's score in either A or B is 25 or more, and he has not yet been diagnosed with ADHD, I recommend that you contact your child's physician or a mental health practitioner to discuss the findings. This can be a key step in obtaining an effective treatment plan for your child.

To get the best results from the Total Focus Program, it's important to use the entire program. If, after reviewing the Behavior Checklist, you find that your child has problems with hyperactivity and impulse control, you may want to emphasize the exercises and audio session in Lesson Five. If the attention and concentration score is higher, it may be helpful to emphasize the exercises and the audio session in Lesson Six.

On the next page, you will find a Progress Chart. Record your child's scores for each section of the Behavior Checklist in the first column of the chart. Then, in one month, I recommend that you fill out the Behavior Checklist again and record the results. It's helpful to do this evaluation after one month, then at three months and then at six months. This will give you a way to actually measure your child's progress with the Total Focus Program and with his overall treatment plan.

 Please record results on the next page.

15

Section	Starting Point	1 Month	3 Months	6 Months
A. Attention/Concentration	30 20 15 10 5	30 20 15 10 5	30 20 15 10 5	30 20 15 10 5
B. Hyperactivity	30 20 15 10 5	30 20 15 10 5	30 20 15 10 5	30 20 15 10 5
C. Behavior/Self-Control	30 20 15 10 5	30 20 15 10 5	30 20 15 10 5	30 20 15 10 5
D. Academic Achievement	30 20 15 10 5	30 20 15 10 5	30 20 15 10 5	30 20 15 10 5

Major Achievements:

1 Month _____

3 Months _____

6 Months _____

Getting Started

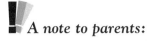 *A note to parents:*

In an ideal world, all members of the family get on board with the Total Focus Program, and it becomes a family project. If all the members of your family are excited about the program and motivated to use it, that's terrific! Because every family is different, this may not always be possible. That's okay. I have seen dramatic success happen in families where the program was championed by one motivated parent and the child with ADHD.

The bottom line is this. Go with everyone who is ready to come along. Do the best you can to get as many family members on board as possible, then move forward with the willing. If that means a team of two—you and your child—that's okay. You, your child, and I will make Total Focus a success.

Step One—To "get focused," the first thing we do is build the team. We do that by having an executive leader meeting. This includes all the adults living in the home, or, as many as are willing to help. All the adults who want to participate should listen to the following:

- Introduction—One-on-One with Dr. Bob
- Bonus Audio—ADHD: First Aid for Parents

Also, each adult participating should fill out a copy of the Behavior Checklist. Review the findings from the checklist at this meeting and compare notes.

Your goal is to identify behaviors or issues that you agree you want your child to work on in the program.

Step Two—The next step is to conduct a family meeting (if you have multiple family members involved) or a one-on-one coaching session with your child (if you will be spearheading the program with your child). Whether you have five people involved or simply two, the guidelines are the same. Our objective is to create an environment where you can communicate more effectively with your child and introduce the program.

I am a big fan of the family meeting. Weekly or monthly family meetings can strengthen the bonds with your children and create better communication all around. I recommend these meetings to start the program, and I recommend that you continue them for as long as you are all living together in the same home.

On the next page you will find general guidelines for family meetings.

TOTAL FOCUS Family Meeting Guidelines

1. Family meetings need to become a regular routine. Same day. Same time. Everybody should attend regularly. No excuses. Commit!

2. Practice Reflective Listening. Everyone needs to be heard and appreciated. Be open. Try to understand the other person's ideas and feelings. Make good eye contact. Let the speaker know you understand and appreciate what he is saying and acknowledge his feelings.

3. Only one person talks at a time. Everyone should listen politely and attentively and patiently await their turn.

4. Avoid negative criticism. Look for positives. Use "I messages" rather than "You messages."

5. Don't argue. Adopt a problem-solving mode where all points of view are considered. Let the group decide on the best way to handle an issue.

6. Develop family meeting traditions for group sharing, such as having each person share one thing that went well for them since the last meeting and one thing that didn't go as well as they would like since the last meeting. Another suggestion is to have each person share a positive statement with each of the other family members.

7. Allow enough time to cover important family and individual concerns. Plan family activities. Discuss the family budget. Find out where each person "IS" in their life.

8. Have FUN! Enjoy each other. Have a sense of humor. End each meeting with family fun time.

The First Family Meeting

- Introduce the meeting as something you're going to do together as a family for a while, and it may become a family tradition. You're doing it to help each member of the family grow.

- Acknowledge some things that you as parents want to work on or improve.

- Ask each child to talk about one thing they would like to see you work on as a parent or with them.

- Ask each child to come up with one thing they would like to change about themselves or work on to improve about themselves.

- Then explain what you would like the kids to work on: "Okay, you've had a turn to tell us something that you thought we should improve. Now it's our turn to talk about what we'd like you to improve."

- Explain to the children that you are going to be using a new program called Total Focus to help everyone in the family get better at what they want to work on. We're going to do it as a family/together.

Important Points:

1.) Mention a point of improvement for each child. With the ADHD child, refer to the behaviors or issues you identified in the Behavior Checklist. (For example: "Brian, we'd like you to work on being more attentive in school and doing things the first time we ask you here at home.")

2.) If you are meeting as a family, DO NOT SINGLE OUT ONE CHILD AS "THE PROBLEM" FOR THE WHOLE FAMILY. Everyone will have something to work on. Not just the ADHD child.

Step Three–Have the child listen to Children's Audio A entitled *Let's Get Focused*. We provide two versions: a lesson for children up to age 10 and one for those 10 and above.

Suggestion: You may want to listen to both lessons before you give them to your child, and choose the one that you feel best fits your child's developmental level.

Many parents enjoy listening to this first lesson with their child, and I would encourage you to do so. It will open doors for discussion about ADHD, behavior issues, and academic performance. Let's Get Focused is designed to give your child a greater understanding of why he thinks and feels the way he does and to let him know that ADHD is a brain difference. Lots of kids have it. By working together with you and me, your child can adapt to this difference and move beyond frustration into achievement.

What's Next?

Once your child has listened to **Let's Get Focused**, you can continue on with Parent's Lesson Two in the workbook. If you have not listened to the Bonus Audio, **ADHD: First Aid for Parents**, now is a good time to do so. We have provided companion materials to this bonus lesson next in the workbook.

Bonus Lesson

Some changes in children with ADHD require time. Others can occur almost instantly. Here are 11 "first aid tips" you can use with an ADHD child that will bring about change quickly. For complete details on how to use these techniques, please listen to the Parent's Bonus Audio in the Total Focus Program.

1. **The First Time Club**–Children with ADHD often have trouble following directions. They are also prone to not doing what is asked of them the first time parents asks. If this is the case with your child, try the First Time Club technique. On page 27, you will find a chart called the *First Time Club Chart*. Place this chart on your refrigerator or in another common area of the home. Explain to your child that you've noticed he has a hard time doing things the first time he is asked. From now on, whenever he does something the first time he is asked, he'll receive a sticker, star, or happy face in one of the squares on the chart. When he gets thirty squares filled up, he will receive a reward. Determine ahead of time what the reward will be. It can be as simple as a trip to his favorite pizza place or renting a movie he's wanted to see. You will be amazed at how easily he can remember to do things "the first time" when the positive reinforcement of a reward is involved.

2. **The "I'm Bored" Collage**–*"I'm bored." "There's nothing here to do." "I don't have anything to do."* ADHD children tire quickly of certain activities and often go from one to the other rapidly. Also, they tend to have difficulty thinking of an activity to follow the one they are completing. If this sounds like your child, get him involved in making an "I'm Bored" Collage. When your child complains he is bored, or at a time when he is calm and not busy with something, give him some poster paper and some magazines and tell him to cut out pictures of things he likes to do: bike riding, books, video games, movies, drawing, play sets, toys, music, computers, etc. Then have your child create a collage using all the things he likes to do. Place the collage in your child's room. Then, whenever he complains of being bored, remind him to go to the collage and pick out an activity he'd like to do. This is a remarkably effective way to stimulate productive thought in an ADHD child. And a good stress reducer for parents. If the "I'm bored" complaint is a real problem in your home, remember that you can offer your child a reward for not saying, "I'm bored" for thirty days.

3. **The High Sign Technique**–ADHD children can be very over-reactive. As a parent, when you are put in the position of having to reprimand your child for being over-reactive, you begin to feel like the proverbial "broken record," and the reprimands are often ineffective. Correcting over-reactive, inappropriate behavior is a particular challenge when you and your child are in public.

That's when The High Sign Technique is useful. Come up with a neutral sign with your child—a signal or secret cue that you can use with your child to let him know he is over-reacting or behaving inappropriately. A halt sign. Pointing to your head (Your secret code for "Stop and think."). A peace sign. Encourage your child to come up with the signal. Then agree that this will be a secret sign the two of you share. And when you give the high sign, it's time for him to settle down. This is a way of communicating your message to the child in a way that doesn't embarrass him or you. And it avoids lecturing, nagging and screaming. It's easier for you and your child.

4. **Catch Them Being Good**—When was the last time you complimented your child on their appearance? When was the last time you thanked your child for doing a chore—even when that chore is something he's been doing for a long time? When your kids are behaving and not bickering and arguing, do you ever stop and say, "Wow, I really like it when you guys get along. Thanks for being so nice to each other." It's human nature for parents to point out when their children are being "bad." But we seldom catch our kids being good. *Positive reinforcement is the key to improving behavior in an ADHD child.* One of the simplest ways to give positive reinforcement is to catch an ADHD child being good. Tonight when you are at home with your child, find something about which you can compliment your child—whether it's brushing his teeth or watching TV quietly with siblings. *When you pay attention to a behavior, it increases. When you ignore a behavior, it decreases.* So, if you want a child with ADHD to increase appropriate behaviors, compliment him. Use selective attention and ignore minor, annoying behaviors that can be overlooked.

5. **The Saturday Box**—If your child is hyperactive or doesn't follow through well with tasks, he may have a tendency to leave his belongings all over the house. When you ask him to pick them up, he might ignore the request (In fact, maybe there are some adults in the home who do the same thing. You're not alone if that's the case.). Here's a solution. Get a large cardboard box, toy box, or plastic storage container from the dollar store or hardware store. Tell everyone that when you find an item lying around that isn't being used and hasn't been put away in its proper place, you're going to put it in the Saturday Box. When an item lands in the Saturday Box, no one can use it until Saturday, when you go in and distribute the items back to their owners and they get put away. You can put this technique to work today with your children. You will notice that when a favorite toy goes in the Saturday Box and your child can't use it until Saturday, he will learn quickly to put his toys away or not leave them lying around. It's also easier on you. No nagging, lecturing, and pointless arguments about dirty socks lying on the floor.

6. **Time to Stop Me**–*"One more time!" "No! Five more minutes!" "I'm not done yet! Don't bug me!"* Children with ADHD, especially when they are younger, often have trouble stopping an activity. Trying to be the "play police" is a losing battle for parents. The more you tell the child to stop, the more objections you get. The solution is to make the clock the cop instead. Use a wind-up kitchen timer. If the child has 10 minutes of play time, tell the child you're going to set the timer for 10 minutes. When the timer goes off, play time is over. Or use the clock. If the child is old enough to tell time, tell them they have 10 minutes of play time and get them to show you when 10 minutes are up. Ask them if they understand. Then tell them to check the hands of the clock. When 10 minutes are up, simply say stop. This technique also helps a child with ADHD to transition from one activity to another. Because they have difficulty stopping, they can be easily frustrated by transitions. A wind-up kitchen timer with a bell provides a kind of demarcation for the child. It helps them to end an activity they find particularly reinforcing.

7. **Grandma's Rule**–You can make the possibility of a low frequency behavior more likely to occur if you make a higher frequency behavior contingent on the occurrence of the low frequency behavior. *Huh?* Here's how Grandma would translate: **WHEN you pick up your clothes, you can go out and play.** When your child wants to do something, make it a reward for doing a chore that needs to be accomplished. Children with ADHD do best when they are given clear, simple one- and two-step directions. So keep the directions simple and use the word "when," not the word "if."
"When you take out the trash, you can watch the video."
"When you take your books off the dinner table, you can have your snack."
Use this the next time you go to the grocery store with your child: *"Show me that you can stop asking for things as we go down the aisles and when we are all through, I'll let you pick out what kind of cereal we buy."*

8. **Time Out the Toy**–When a child with ADHD wants to get your attention, he will get it by whatever means necessary, including annoying you with a toy. A toy gun he keeps popping off in the house. A tool set with a hammer he keeps pounding on the coffee table. A trike that gets banged into the living room furniture over and over again. A game that always seems to cause an argument between siblings. You can give the child a timeout, certainly. But there will likely be many infractions that will mean another timeout for the child. Instead, give the toy a timeout. Simply say, "I have asked you to control the toy, but it seems to be having a problem still. So I will have to give the toy a timeout for the rest of the day." The child will not be able to use the toy for the rest of the day. When you let the toy "out of timeout," remind the child that he has to control the toy, or it will go into a longer timeout next time. Sometimes giving the toy a timeout is easier for parents. And the child learns that he has to take responsibility for his behavior—and for his things—if he wants to avoid a negative consequence.

9. **Pick Your Battles–**An ADHD child will try to engage you in many "battles" as he grows up. As a parent, you need to choose those battles. Some battles over minor infractions simply aren't worth fighting. In fact, if you don't fight them, you will find that the annoyance will probably go away. With an ADHD child who is over-reactive, responding to a minor inappropriate behavior can make it seem more important to the child and the inappropriate behavior will increase. Whereas, if you ignore it, it will likely decrease and fade away to nothing. It is certainly up to the parent to determine what is major, what is minor, and what is extremely minor. The point is, let go of some of the extremely minor stuff, and your child will very likely let go of some of his irritating behaviors.

10. **Counting to Ten–**We know that the emotional regulation system doesn't work properly in the brain of an ADHD child. That's why they tend to over-react, throw tantrums and have outbursts. I suggest implementing the Counting to Ten technique with your entire family. At a family meeting, make it a rule that "in our family, when we are angry and we want to spout off and yell at someone or call them a nasty name, instead, from now on, we are going to stop and count to ten silently." By counting to ten, we are forcing ourselves to stop and think. This will benefit you, the ADHD child, and the sibling who feels an injustice from the ADHD child and wants to retaliate. Counting to ten disengages the emotional part of the brain and forces the thinking part of the brain into action. It also helps to trigger the relaxation response. What follows counting to ten will most likely be more constructive than cursing, name calling, or tantrums. Give this technique a try the next time you feel annoyed with your child, and encourage your child to use it with you and with siblings.

11. **Let's Remember the Rules–**This technique works well for older children (perhaps age 9 or 10), who don't respond to timeouts because they think they're "too old." If the rule in the home is that you do not talk back to your parents, explain to the child that when this rule is broken, he will need to write down the rule in order to help him remember. "I will not talk back to my parents." The first time you forget the rule, you will need to write it down five times. If you forget it again the same day, you will need to write it down ten times. This is a form of negative consequence known as "mass practice." And it works. I have used it in my own home and in therapy with kids with ADHD. When you do this every time the behavior occurs, the child quickly gets the point that he needs to remember the rules. And he would rather obey those rules than have to write them down over and over again. For you, it means no screaming and a simple solution to the problem that is firm, fair, friendly...and effective.

    Remember that you can change many negative habit patterns in an ADHD child by offering the child a reward for engaging in a new behavior that is positive. It's the principle behind The First Time Club. If your child pouts or cries when you tell him no and nothing you've tried has changed that behavior, use the *I Can Do It Chart* on page 29. Tell him he will receive a sticker or happy face in a square for each day he can go without pouting or crying. Let him know he will receive a reward when he can get 30 squares filled.

TOTAL FOCUS First Time Club

_____ is working to become a member of the First Time Club.

To become a member, you must be able to do what you are asked right away the first time you are asked.

Every time you do something the first time asked, a square on the chart will be filled with a _____ .

When ALL the squares on the chart are filled you will become a member of the club and receive

_____ .

TOTAL FOCUS   **I Can Do It!**

_____ is working on _____ .
Every time you do this, a square on the chart will be filled with a _____ . When ALL the squares are filled, you will receive _____ for a reward.

52 Stress Reducers for Parents

You can reduce the stresses of parenting by making small adjustments that reduce the stresses of your life in general. Here are 52 easy ways to do it.

1. Get up fifteen minutes earlier in the morning. The inevitable morning mishaps will be less stressful.

2. Prepare for the morning the evening before. Set the breakfast table, make lunches, put out the clothes you plan to wear, etc.

3. Don't rely on your memory. Write down appointment times, when to pick up the laundry, when library books are due, etc. ("The palest ink is better than the most retentive memory." -Old Chinese Proverb)

4. Don't do anything that leads you to tell a lie.

5. Make duplicates of all keys. Bury a house key in a secret spot in the garden, and carry a duplicate car key in your wallet, apart from your key ring.

6. Practice preventive maintenance. Your car, appliances, home and relationships will be less likely to break down/fall apart "at the worst possible moment."

7. Be prepared to wait. A paperback can make a wait in a post office line almost pleasant.

8. Procrastination is stressful. Whatever you want to do tomorrow, do today; whatever you want to do today, do it now.

9. Plan ahead. Don't let the gas tank get below one-quarter full. Keep a well-stocked emergency shelf of home staples. Don't wait until you're down to your last bus token or postage stamp to buy more, etc.

10. Don't put up with something that doesn't work right. If your alarm clock, wallet, shoe laces, wind-shield wipers, whatever are a constant aggravation, get them fixed or get new ones.

11. Allow 15 minutes of extra time to get to appointments. Plan to arrive at an airport two hours before domestic departures.

12. Eliminate (or restrict) the amount of caffeine in your diet.

13. Always set up contingency plans, "just in case." ("If for some reason either of us is delayed, here's what we'll do." Or, "If we get split up in the shopping center, here's where we'll meet.")

14. Relax your standards. The world will not end if the grass doesn't get mowed this weekend.

15. Pollyanna-Power! For every one thing that goes wrong, there are probably 10 or 50 or 100 blessings. Count'em!

16. Ask questions. Taking a few moments to repeat back directions, what someone expects of you, etc., can save hours. (The old "the hurrieder I go, the behinder I get," idea.)

17. Say "No!" Saying "no" to extra projects, social activities, and invitations you know you don't have the time or energy for takes practice, self-respect, and a belief that everyone, everyday, needs quiet time to relax and be alone.

18. Unplug your phone. Want to take a long bath, sleep, or read without interruption? Drum up the courage to temporarily disconnect. (The possibility of there being a terrible emergency in the next hour or so is almost nil). Or use an answering machine.

19. Turn needs into preferences. Our basic physical needs translate into food, water, and keeping warm. Everything else is a preference. Don't get attached to preferences.

20. Simplify, simplify, simplify...

21. Make friends with non-worriers. Nothing can get you into the habit or worrying faster than associating with chronic worrywarts.

22. Get up and stretch periodically if your job requires that you sit for extended periods.

23. Wear earplugs. If you need to find quiet at home, pop in some earplugs.

24. Get enough sleep. If necessary, use an alarm clock to remind you to go to bed.

25. Create order out of chaos. Organize your home and workspace so that you always know exactly where things are. Put things away where they belong, and you won't have to go through the stress of losing things.

26. When feeling stressed, most people tend to breathe in short, shallow breaths. When you breathe like this, stale air is not expelled, oxidation of the tissues is incomplete and muscle tension frequently results. Check your breathing throughout the day and before, during, and after high pressure situations. If you find your stomach muscles are knotted, and your breathing is shallow, relax all your muscles and take several deep, slow breaths. Note how, when you're relaxed, both your abdomen and chest expand when you breathe.

27. Writing your thoughts and feelings down (in a journal, or a paper to be thrown away) can help you clarify things and can give you a renewed perspective.

28. Try the following yoga technique whenever you feel the need to relax. Inhale deeply through your nose to the count of eight. Then with lips puckered, exhale very slowly through your mouth to the count of 15 or for as long as you can. Concentrate on the long sighing sound and feel the tension dissolve. Repeat 10 times.

29. Inoculate yourself against a feared event. For example, before speaking in public, take time to go over every part of the experience in your mind. Imagine what you'll wear, what the audience will look like, how you will present your talk, what the questions will be, and how you will answer them, etc. Visualize the experience the way you would have it be. You'll likely find that when the time comes to make the actual presentation, it will be "old hat" and much of your anxiety will have fled.

30. When the stress of having to get a job done gets in the way of getting the job done, diversion (a voluntary change in activity and/or environment) may be just what you need.

31. Talk it out. Discussing your problems with a trusted friend can help clear your mind of confusion so you can concentrate on problem solving.

32. One of the most obvious ways to avoid unnecessary stress is to select an environment (work, home, leisure) which is in line with your personal needs and desires. If you hate desk jobs, don't accept a job which requires that you sit at a desk all day. If you hate to talk politics, don't associate with people who love to talk politics, etc.

33. Learn to live one day at a time.

34. Every day, do something you really enjoy.

35. Add an ounce of love to everything you do.

36. Take a hot bath or shower (or a cool one in the summertime) to relieve tension.

37. Do something for somebody else. Make a meal for someone who is in need.

38. Focus on understanding rather than on being understood; on loving rather than on being loved.

39. Do something that will improve your appearance. Looking better can help you feel better.

40. Schedule a realistic day. Avoid the tendency to schedule back-to-back appointments. Allow time between appointments for a breathing spell.

41. Become more flexible. Some things are worth not doing perfectly, and some issues are okay to compromise upon.

42. Eliminate destructive self-talk: "I'm too old to...," "I'm too fat to...," etc.

43. Use your weekend time for a change of pace. If your work week is slow and patterned, make sure there is action and time for spontaneity built into your weekends. If your work week is fast-paced and full of people and deadlines, seek peace and solitude during your days off. Feel as if you are not accomplishing anything at work? Tackle a job on the weekend that you can finish to your satisfaction.

44. "Worry about the pennies and the dollars will take of themselves." That's another way of saying: take care of the todays as best you can and the yesterdays and the tomorrows will take care of themselves.

45. Do one thing at a time. When you are with someone, be with that person and with no one or anything else. When you are busy with a project, concentrate on doing that project and forget about everything else you have to do.

46. Allow yourself time–everyday–for privacy, quiet, and introspection.

47. If an especially unpleasant task faces you, do it early in the day and get it over with. Then, the rest of your day will be free of anxiety.

48. Learn to delegate responsibility to capable others.

49. Don't forget to take a lunch break. Try to get away from your desk or work area in body and mind, even if it's just for 15 or 20 minutes.

50. Forget about counting to 10. Count to 1,000 before doing something or saying anything that could make matters worse.

51. Have a forgiving view of events and people. Accept the fact that we live in an imperfect world.

52. Have an optimistic view of the world. Believe that most people are doing the best they can.

On Task and In Control at School

Behavior modification uses what psychologists call "contingency management" to change a child's behavior in a desired direction. It has been used successfully for many years as a useful tool in treating ADHD in children and adolescents. In behavior modification, you establish a system to provide incentives—positive reinforcement—for appropriate behavior, and sometimes consequences or negative reinforcement for inappropriate behavior. The system is used to progressively shape the behavior by working to achieve small changes in the desired direction and eventually getting to the ultimate goal for the program. In this lesson, we will use behavior modification to improve your child's performance at school.

Some research has concluded that behavior modification alone can be all that is necessary to satisfactorily improve behavior and academic achievement. It appears that, in some cases, external reward can provide the motivation necessary for the child to develop the internal resources on his own to accomplish the goals. Behavior modification has been used successfully to treat a wide variety of psychological disorders with children and adults.

❗ *In my experience, the best behavioral approach to help a child with ADHD is to reward the desired behavior and essentially ignore inappropriate behavior.* Basically, if a child is focused on completing a task or being involved in a classroom activity, he is less likely to produce behavior that is disruptive to the classroom. Behavior modification programs that center only on punishing inappropriate behavior do not work well with ADHD students. Incidentally, when the goals are reached, and the child "graduates" from the program, you will find that regular rewards will no longer be necessary to maintain the results.

PROGRAM A (FOR CHILDREN TO AGE 10)
Note: If your child is over age 10, you can skip to Program B on page 36.

This program works extremely well with this age group. I have seen many children dramatically improve their classroom behavior as well as their task completion just by carefully implementing this program. You will use the **School Success Charts** for this portion of the program. You will find these in your Total Focus Program bound together in a tear-off pad so you will have plenty available.

The reason this program is so effective with younger children is because it breaks the school day down into six periods such as reading, math, music, or before recess, before lunch etc. Most programs are based on the whole day. If the child has a major problem at the beginning of the day, he knows he has "blown it" and has no incentive to try to improve during the rest of the day. With this program, a child may have several periods where he does not meet the criteria to earn a happy face on his School Success Chart, but he may need to earn only one or two to earn his reward. Thus, he is not discouraged by the lack of reward for a given period, but is encouraged to try harder the next period. The instructions for using the School Success Chart are provided right on the charts themselves. Give one of the School Success Charts to your child's teacher during your conference prior to starting the program.

Here are the basic steps necessary to carry out this portion of the school program:

Meet with your child's teacher:

Request his cooperation in carrying out the program.

Let him know that this program is only one part of a comprehensive treatment program.

Give him a copy of the **School Success Chart**. Explain that it is important that he only place a happy face in the appropriate square for each period the child meets the task completion criteria. Ask him not to use unhappy faces or write notes in a square when the criteria are not met. He is to leave the square blank.

Review the criteria related to task completion. In order to earn a happy face for a given period of instruction, the child should display one or more of the following behaviors as appropriate for that particular period:

- Complete the written assignment.
- Read quietly. Listen to the discussion.
- Participate appropriately in the class activity.
- Wait his turn quietly to be called upon to answer a question.

Establish a "Base Line"

- Have the teacher complete the School Success Chart for one week. During this week, the teacher DOES NOT show the chart to the child.
- Compute the daily average "happy faces per day." (Total for the week divided by five)
- Take the daily average and add 1. This becomes the goal for Level 1 of the program. (If the child earned an average of two happy per faces per day, then the goal will be to earn three per day).

Meet with your child:

Explain the purpose of the system. Explain to him that this program will reward his good work during class.

Tell him that the program will continue until he is able to go four weeks receiving a minimum of five out of six happy faces per day.

Select the reward he will earn each day he gets the required number of happy faces. Some possible rewards would include, extra TV time, time to go out and ride bikes, extra time playing video games, extra time listening to music, extra roller blade or skateboard time, extra time on the computer, choosing dessert, staying up 15 minutes later at night, playing a game with parents selected by the child.

(Children as well as adults will lose interest in a reward. You will have to select a new reward from time to time to keep the program going. See the list of rewards in the Appendix for a list of reward suggestions.)

On a daily basis, review the criteria for receiving a happy face during a period of instruction. Help the child to memorize the list. Also, tell him how well he is doing.

! Note: *Tell your child that failing to bring home the School Success Chart each day will result in zero happy faces for the day.*

WEEKLY REVIEW:

- Total points for the week.
- Discuss progress.
- Praise accomplishments.
- Provide weekly reward when earned.
- Record progress on the Progress Chart found in this chapter.
- After the child has earned the weekly reward for two weeks, move up to Level 2.
  (Adjust the goals by increasing the number of happy faces to earn the reward by one per day)
- Repeat the changes in levels until the goal of getting six out of six is reached.

Plan a "graduation party" to celebrate completing the program.

PROGRAM B (FOR CHILDREN AGE 10 AND ABOVE)

This program is designed to work with an older age group. The goal is to gradually shape classroom behavior toward the desired goal. I have used this program very successfully with this age group. It is important to attempt to gain the full cooperation of all the child's teachers. **The Daily Student Rating Cards** used in this system are designed to give you, the parent, daily information on your child's performance in a variety of areas of academic functioning from all of his teachers. The cards are included in your program in a tear-off pad so you will have plenty available.

Every day, your child should take the Daily Student Rating Card to school with him and give it to each of his teachers that day. The card should be given to the teacher at the end of each class period. The teacher is then to mark on the card either the number "1" if the child met a criteria or a zero "0" if he did not. If the item was not applicable for that day (e.g. no homework was done) they are given a number 1. The areas on the card involve class participation, class work, homework, and interactions with other children. After rating the child, the teacher is to initial at the bottom of the column underneath his ratings. This is to insure that these are indeed the teacher's ratings. There is room on the card for up to six teachers to evaluate the child each day. If the child has one teacher per day, then that teacher should rate the child after each period of instruction (reading, math, social studies, etc.). At the end of school, the child is to return the card home. Failure to return the card means no rewards that day.

When the child comes home, the parent should first look over the card and provide the child with praise for all the number "1s" earned for that day. If the child's marks are particularly poor, the parent should question the child at that time as to the reason for the poor performance. Also, help him to come up with ways to improve his performance.

After adding up the points the child has received that day, the parent then tells the child how many points he has earned for that school day. The child can earn a maximum of 24 points per day. The child is to use the total points for that day to purchase his privileges around the home. A larger reward is established for the weekend, and is based on the total points earned for the entire week (a maximum of 120).

Here are the basic steps necessary to carry out this portion of the program:

Meet with your child's teachers:

Request their cooperation in carrying out the program.

Let them know that this program is only one part of a comprehensive treatment program.

Let them review a copy of the *Daily Student Rating Card*.

Meet with your child:

Explain the purpose of the system. Explain to him that this program will reward his good work during class.

Tell him that the program will continue until he is able to go four weeks receiving 22 or more points per day.

Select the reward(s) he will earn each day he gets the required number of points. Some possible rewards would include: extra TV time, extra bike riding time, extra time playing video games, extra roller blade or skateboard time, extra time on the computer, choosing dessert, staying up 30 minutes later at night, extra cell phone/texting time. (You may need to agree on time limits for some of these activities). You will find more suggestions for rewards in the Appendix.

EXAMPLE

TV per 1/2 hour	2 points
Bike for day	4 points
Skateboard for day	4 points
Cell phone per 1/2 hour	2 points
Computer time per 1/2 hour	2 points

Select the larger reward(s) for the weekend. The child can use up to the total points he earned during the week on the weekend. Some possible rewards would include, McDonalds, going to the park, having a friend overnight, going to a friend's house overnight, going to a movie, renting a video or a video game. (Children as well as adults will lose interest in a reward. You will have to select a new reward from time to time to keep the program going). See the Appendix for a list of reward suggestions.

EXAMPLE		
	McDonalds	40 points
	Friend overnight	30 points
	Rent a video or video game	20 points
	Stay up late	20 points

Note: Tell your child that failing to bring home the Daily Student Rating Card each day will results in zero points for the day.

On a daily basis, review the criteria for receiving all four points during a period of instruction. Help the child to memorize the list. Also, tell him how well he is doing.

- Participate appropriately in class activities.
- Complete all classroom assignments.
- Hand in all homework to the teacher.
- Show friendly attitude toward other students.

WEEKLY REVIEWS
- Review progress for the week.
- Record progress on the Progress Chart, found in this chapter.
- Praise accomplishments.
- Provide weekly reward(s) when earned.

Plan a "graduation party" to celebrate completing the program.

Almost all children find this system to be quite rewarding after they have used it for several days. In addition, many begin to develop a new attitude towards school because of their ability to earn extra privileges by performing well in school on any particular day. Thus, this program is quite a positive program for most children rather than a punitive one.

TOTAL FOCUS

PROGRESS CHART

Program A

Points	Week 1	Week 2	Week 3	Week 4	Week 5	Week 6	Week 7	Week 8	Week 9	Week 10
30										
29										
28										
27										
26										
25										
24										
23										
22										
21										
20										
19										
18										
17										
16										
15										
14										
13										
12										
11										
10										
9										
8										
7										
6										
5										
4										
3										
2										
1										

Make several copies of this chart. For each week, color in the squares equal to the daily average of the total points earned for that week. (Total points for the week divided by 5)

TOTAL FOCUS

PROGRESS CHART

Program B

Points	Week 1	Week 2	Week 3	Week 4	Week 5	Week 6	Week 7	Week 8	Week 9	Week 10
24										
23										
22										
21										
20										
19										
18										
17										
16										
15										
14										
13										
12										
11										
10										
9										
8										
7										
6										
5										
4										
3										
2										
1										

Make several copies of this chart. For each week, color in the squares equal to the daily average of the total points earned for that week. (Total points for the week divided by 5)

Homework Tips for Parents

Certain key practices will make life easier for everyone in the family when it comes to study time and study organization. However, some of them may require an adjustment for other members of the family.

Turn off the TV!

Make a house rule, depending on the location of the set, that when it is study time, it is "no TV" time. A television set that is on will draw youngsters like bees to honey.

What about music?

Should it be on or off? Contrary to what many specialists say, some youngsters do seem to function well with music playing. (Depending on the layout of your house or apartment, and the type of listening device, maybe an investment in earphones would be worthy of consideration.)

Set rules about phone calls during study hours.

The more people in the household, the more restrictions on long and unnecessary phone calls are needed. A timer, placed next to the phone, can help to control the length of calls so that the telephone will be available if it becomes necessary to call a schoolmate to confirm an assignment or discuss particularly difficult homework.

Designate specific areas for homework and studying.

Possibilities include the child's room or the kitchen or dining room table. Eliminate as much distraction as possible.

Since many young people will study in their own rooms, function becomes more important than beauty. Most desks for young people really don't have sufficient space to spread out materials. A table that allows for all necessary supplies such as pencils, pens, paper, books, and other essentials works extremely well.

Consider placing a bulletin board in your child's room. You can buy a cork board at an office supply store. Use it to post assignments, reminders, excellent papers, awards, a calendar with assignments and projects, etc.

Encourage the use of a small book or pad for writing down assignments so that there is no confusion about when certain assignments must be turned in to the teacher.

Keeping general supplies on hand is important. Check with your child about his needs. In fact, make it his responsibility to be well supplied with paper, pencils, note pads, notebook paper, etc.

Regularity is a key factor in academic success.

Try to organize the household so that supper is served at a standard time, and once it and family discussions are over, it's time to crack the books. If the student doesn't have other commitments and gets home reasonably early from school, some homework can be done before supper.

Consider your child's developmental level when setting the amount of time for homework. While high school students can focus for over an hour, first-graders are unlikely to last more than 15 minutes on a single task. Allow your child to take breaks, perhaps as a reward for finishing a section of the work.

Organize study and homework projects.

Get a large calendar, one that allows space for jotting down things in the daily boxes. Rip it apart so that you (and the child) can sequentially mount the school months for the current semester. For example, you can tear off September, October, November, December, and January and mount them from left to right across one wall. Have the child use a bold color writing instrument (felt tip pen) to mark exam dates in one color, reports that are coming due in a different color, etc. This will serve as a reminder so that things aren't set aside until the last dangerous moment.

Teach your child that studying is more than just doing homework assignments.

One of the most misunderstood aspects of schoolwork is the difference between studying and doing homework assignments. Encourage your child to do things like:

- take notes as he's reading a chapter
- learn to skim material
- learn to study tables and charts
- learn to summarize what he has read in his own words
- learn to make his own flashcards for quick review of dates, formulas, spelling words, etc.

Note-taking is a critical skill and should be developed.

Many students don't know how to take notes in those classes that require them. Some feel they have to write down every word the teacher says. Others have wisely realized the value of an outline form of note-taking. Well prepared teachers present their material in a format that lends itself to outline form note taking.

Should notes ever be rewritten?

In some cases, they should be, particularly if a lot of material was covered, and the youngster had to write quickly but lacks speed and organization. Rewriting notes takes time, but it can be an excellent review of the subject matter. However, rewriting notes isn't worth the time unless they are used for review and recall of important information.

A home dictionary is essential.

However, if it is kept on a shelf to gather dust, it won't do anyone any good. Keep it in an accessible place and let your child see you refer to it from time to time. If the family dictionary is kept in the living room and the child studies in his room, get him an inexpensive dictionary for his exclusive use.

Good dictionary, encyclopedia and organizational skills depend on the ability to alphabetize. See if your child's teacher practices alphabetizing in class. Try alphabetizing spelling words, family members' names or a few favorite toys at home as a way of practicing.

Help your child to feel confident for tests.

Taking tests can be a traumatic experience for some students. Explain to your child that burning the midnight oil (cramming) the night before a test is not productive. Better to get a good night's sleep. Students also need reminding that when taking a test, they should thoroughly and carefully read the directions before they haphazardly start to mark their test papers. They should be advised to skip over questions for which they don't know the answers. They can always return to those if there's time. Good advice for any student before taking a test: take a deep breath, relax, and dive in. Always bring an extra pencil just in case.

During a homework session, watch for signs of frustration.

No learning can take place and little can be accomplished if the child is angry or upset over an assignment that is too long or too difficult. At such times, the parent may have to step in and simply halt the homework for that night, offering to write a note to the teacher explaining the situation and perhaps requesting a conference to discuss the quality and length of homework assignments.

Should parents help with homework?

Yes. If it is clearly productive to do so, such as calling out spelling words or checking a math problem that won't prove. No. If it is something the child can clearly handle himself and learn from the process. And help and support should always be calmly and cheerfully given. Grudging help is worse than no help at all!

Read directions, or check over math problems after your child has completed the work. Remember to make positive comments. You don't want your child to associate homework with fights at home.Model research skills by involving your child in planning a family trip. Help your child locate your destination on a map or atlas. Use an online encyclopedia or a CD-ROM to find information about the place you will visit; try the Internet or books in the library.

How best to handle report cards.

To save shocks and upsets, gently discuss from time to time "how things are going at school" with your child. Something casual, such as "How did the math test go?" "How did you do on the history report?" "How's your science project coming along? Need any help?" are questions that aren't "third degree" but indicate interest. Find out if it is a policy at your child's school to send out "warning notices" when work isn't going well. Generally, such notices require the parent's signature to verify that the parent has, indeed, been alerted. This is the time to contact the teacher of the course, along with your child, to learn what the difficulty may be. If such notices aren't sent, then grades on projects and reports and from tests may be the sole source of information short of what your child wishes to share.

Be tuned in to statements such as "He's an awful teacher," "She goes too fast," etc. This may be the child's way of indicating frustration in understanding content or lack of study time with the subject. However, be cautious in contacting teachers without your child's approval or interest. It may disrupt good feelings between you and make you seem to be interfering and spying.

Getting The Assignments Home and Turned In:

ADHD children have a reputation for "forgetting" to bring assignments home. Even when they remember to bring home assignments, they often forget to bring home necessary books or other materials to complete the assignments. Finally, it is not unusual for the ADHD child to complete assignments at home and then forget to turn them in when they get to school the next day. The problems are probably more related to lack of organization than a faulty memory. The following guidelines can be useful in solving these homework problems:

1. Get a large, three ring notebook with a clip on the back cover. Insert organization folders for each subject.

   - Use the folders to keep class notes, worksheets and assignments that are currently in progress.

   - Use the clip at the back cover to place completed homework assignments that are to be turned in to the teacher. Each day the clip should be checked before leaving the school campus. Any assignments left should be taken to the teacher before leaving the campus.

2. Make copies of the Daily Assignment Schedule found on the next page.

   - Place a new copy in the front of the notebook each day.

   - Teach your child how to write down assignments. (You can hold a practice session at home. Give the assignments orally and/or write them down on a "black board." Your child should be able to accurately write down the daily assignments.

   - Meet with your child's teacher(s) and ask them for their help with this project. They should initial the DAS each day to indicate that the list of assignments is accurate and complete. Hopefully they will work with your child to help them become good assignment recorders.

3. Go over the Daily Assignment Schedule before starting on homework. Help your child learn to decide how much time each assignment may take and make up a homework schedule for the day. Add any long-term assignments such as test preparation, essays, book reports or science projects to your master calendar.

4. Go over the list at the end of all homework sessions and check them off on the Daily Assignment Schedule. Make sure they get attached to the clip on the back of the notebook.

TOTAL FOCUS

DAILY ASSIGNMENT SCHEDULE

Date: __/__/__
Day: ___

Subject	Assignment Details	Materials Needed	Teacher's Initials	Parent's Initials

Special Requests:_____
_____
_____
_____

47

In Focus

- Behavior modification uses positive reinforcement and incentives to change a child's behavior and shape it in a desired direction.

- Your child's teacher will use the simple forms provided in the Total Focus Program to give your child immediate feedback on his ability to stay on task, complete assignments and cooperate in school.

- The number of happy faces or points accrued each day will be used to obtain or "purchase" rewards or privileges at home.

- When your child is constantly focused on working to achieve the reward, he is behaving appropriately, staying on task, and completing assignments. These are the desired behaviors.

What's Next?

After you have begun the school behavior modification program, I recommend that you and your child listen to the track on Children's Audio B called *3 Secrets for School Success*. Have your child fill out the *I Am Good At...*motivational sheet on page 51 of the workbook. I've also provided a summary sheet of the *3 Secrets for School Success* here in the workbook. You may want to hang this in your child's room or encourage him to carry it in his notebook. Then, when you're ready, continue on with Parent's Lesson Three in the workbook.

Tip: The cards I refer to in 3 Secrets for School Success are found on page 101. Feel free to review and use them with your child now or wait until we move on to Lesson Four. I also refer to "brain training" in 3 Secrets for School Success. This is simply to help prepare your child for the exercises he'll be doing soon in Lessons Five and Six. More on these exercises later.

TOTAL FOCUS

I Am Good At...

1. _____

_____

2. _____

_____

3. _____

_____

I Am Going to Get Better At:

1. _____

_____

2. _____

_____

3. _____

_____

"I can do it if I try. If I try, and keep working on it, then I can be better and better in every way every day."

- Dr. Bob

TOTAL FOCUS **3 Secrets for School Success**

1. Stop the Stinking Thinking - Start Smart Talking.

Don't say: "I can't do this."
Say: "I am having trouble,
but I can get it or I can ask for help."

Don't say: "I'm no good at anything."
Say: "I am good at many things,
but not everything, and that's OK."

2. Work with the team.

Coach: My teachers
Trainers: My parents
Cheerleaders and Fans: My family and my friends
Me: The Star Player
Working with the team will make me a winner!

3. Be Prepared and Build Myself Up

Relax
Practice Brain Training
Have an "I Can" Attitude

TOTAL FOCUS Homework Help	
Basic Rules	**Great Homework Help on the Web**
1. Have a quiet place for homework that has all the materials you need (pens, pencils, markers, paper, etc.)	• Kid Info–A single source with links to help for all subjects. *www.kidinfo.com*
2. Stick with a regular time or times each day to do homework.	• Fact Monster–This is a nationally recognized kid's site for individualized homework help, reference materials, fun facts and features. *www.factmonster.com*
3. Take a break between subjects.	• Searching for Stuff–Kid's search tools. *www.slcolibrary.org/kz/index.htm*
4. When you get stuck on an assignment, take a break and go to another assignment and then come back to the tough assignment later.	• Wikipedia–Free encyclopedia that anyone can edit. *www.wikipedia.org*
5. When you start to get uptight – RELAX.	• `Museums in the USA *www.museumca.org/usa/*
6. When you start to get upset – change your thoughts from "Stinking Thinking" to" Smart Talk." (Change "I can't" to "I can.")	• Biography.com *www.biography.com*
7. Review your work. Say the main points aloud. Make up flash cards to study key facts for a test.	• Merriam-Webster's Dictionary *www.m-w.com*
8. Don't be afraid to ask parents or others for help. Don't wait until the last minute to ask for help.	• Cool Science for Curious Kids *www.hhmi.org/coolscience/*
9. Try to do your best. But remember that no one is perfect. You will do better on some assignments than others. That's OK.	• How Stuff Works–Find out how the engine in your car works, or what gears do, or what makes the inside of your refrigerator cold. *www.howstuffworks.com*
10. Figure out a system to help you remember to turn in your assignments when you get to school. A clip in the back of your notebook or a special folder in your backpack are two possibilities.	• Super Science Fair Projects–Complete guide to science fair projects, topics and experiments. *www.super-science-fair-projects.com*
	• Google Earth–Maps and satellite images *www.earth.google.com*
	• Count On–Teaches a variety of math skills for all ages and abilities. *www.counton.org*

Relaxation/Biofeedback
To Improve Attention, Self-Control, and Relationships

How To Use Relaxation Training

Relaxation training is very effective with children and teenagers. I have found that it is particularly effective with children age seven and above. With younger children, you should introduce them to this technique, and then decide after a few sessions if your child is able to benefit from relaxation training.

I suggest that you and your child practice the following simple relaxation exercises. When you have the hang of it, then go to the Biofeedback Exercises in this lesson.

Relaxation Exercises to Practice with Your Child

I'd like to teach you some simple relaxation techniques to trigger the relaxation response. I suggest that you use them on your own and with your child. Remember that you cannot be relaxed and stressed at the same time. You are either one or the other. These techniques help your body to return to a state of relaxation. As you will see, these techniques only take a few minutes. I've designed them to be very simple and very easy to fit into your day. And I believe you will find them to be a very rewarding thing to do with your child.

When you are practicing these relaxation techniques, it's best to breathe in through the nose and out through the mouth. If you have to do mouth breathing, that's ok. But it's much better to breathe in through the nose and out through the mouth.

Quiet Time. The first technique is one I call Quiet Time. With this technique, your child can have some fun listening to their own breathing. Most kids think this is fun and, of course, you can sit and do it right along with them, listening to your own breath. Or you can watch them practice. All you have to do is say, "We're going to start improving how we breathe because this is how our body takes in oxygen. We're going to listen to how we do this and learn how to breathe more deeply, which means our body and brain get more oxygen. And that means everything will work better, and we'll have more energy, power and strength. Quiet Time helps us to learn to go on a little vacation and regroup. When we're through, we'll feel just like we have been on a vacation. Now we're going to just sit and be quiet. See how long we can be quiet and just listen to our breathing in and breathing out. Just listen and be quiet. And we're going to do this for a couple of minutes each day."

I suggest you do the Quiet Time breathing exercise once a day for about a week. You can also tell your child that as we do it each day, we're just allowing ourselves to let go and just be aware of our own breathing. Look around and be aware of things around you, and you'll find that maybe you see something, hear something, or smell something that you didn't before you started practicing.

Diaphragmatic or "Belly Button" Breathing. After we've done quiet time for a few days (up to a week) then we move on to stomach breathing, technically known as diaphragmatic breathing. For kids, you can just call it "Belly Button Breathing." Diaphragmatic breathing for children and adults is a great way to release tension. It also develops deeper breathing, which can have a lot of value for sports and singing and other activities Again, I suggest that you find a quiet place where the child can lie on the floor. Go ahead and do it with them. This is a chance for you both to relax. You can either place your hands on your stomach just below the rib cage, or you can place an object there instead, such as a little book or a stuffed animal. Something that allows you to see the diaphragm working. Then say, "Now we're going to practice breathing with our belly button. We're going to take in a deep breath and practice breathing until we can see the book, teddy bear, whatever it is on the stomach, go up and down." Breathe in and out 10 to 20 times when you practice this. I suggest that you practice this technique for a week or so. It's also a good idea to practice this from time to time maybe just with your hand on your stomach rather than an object just to be sure that you still have this skill down.

Elevator Breathing. This is a form of visualization to help stay focused and centered and practice moving the breath to all parts of the body. You can do this technique either lying down or sitting in a cross-legged position. Start out by having the child sit and breathe naturally. After he has practiced breathing naturally, say, "Now, I want you to imagine that your breath is like an elevator taking a ride through your body. We're going to start by breathing through your nose to start our ride on the elevator. So once you've breathed in, then breathe out and you can feel your breath go all the way to the basement, down to your feet, to your toes. Now you can breathe in and take your elevator breath up to your belly button. Hold it. Now breathe out all your air. This time, breathe in and take your elevator breath up to your chest. Hold it. Breathe out all your air. Now, breathe in and take your elevator breath up to the top floor. Up through your throat into your face and forehead. Feel your head fill with the breath. Hold it. Now, breathe out and feel your elevator breath take all your troubles and worries down through your chest, your belly, your legs and out the elevator door in your feet." Chances are, this will be really fun for your child. Kids love this. So do it again with them. This is something that you can do once a day for another week or so.

Tip: You can use the exercise on your Bonus CD called General Relaxation for the Whole Family with your child as well. This is an excellent exercise to use, especially after you have practiced the three techniques discussed above. The General Relaxation exercise uses progressive relaxation, where we progressively relax all the areas of the body. This is fun for you to do with your child. It's calming for kids and a wonderful stress reducer for parents.

Directions for Biofeedback Training

You have been provided with a **Stress Sensor Card** which has a temperature sensor, along with a color chart to enable you to understand what the **Stress Sensor Card** is telling you. You will see by looking at the chart that the colors black and red indicate low skin temperature, while the colors green and blue indicate high skin temperature. The Stress Sensor Card provides what is called biofeedback. Biofeedback refers to a procedure that provides information about a body function. In this case, we are measuring skin temperature, which is a measure of a body function known as peripheral circulation. This biofeedback procedure is known as temperature biofeedback.

Warm skin temperature is associated with relaxation, while colder skin temperature is associated with stress and tension. When we are relaxed, our brain produces more alpha waves, which are associated with synchronizing the two hemispheres of the brain. With increased alpha waves, we are better able to focus and pay attention. We are also better able to tune out distraction. Children who are relaxed are also less hyperactive and have better self-control.

Learning how to control how relaxed you are and thus raising the skin temperature may not be as easy as you might think. However, with practice, a person can learn to have good control of this function. Gradually children or adults can learn to achieve a complete state of relaxation without needing to use the Stress Sensor Card. I encourage parents to use the Stress Sensor Card along with their children. It helps the parent understand what the child is learning to do, while also helping the parent to learn a technique that is wonderful for coping with stress and managing anger.

1. Please read the directions provided with the Stress Sensor Card. The child should then hold the **Stress Sensor Card** while placing his thumb on the temperature sensor patch. After about 10 seconds, make a mental note of the color of the temperature sensor on the Stress Sensor Card. Have him close his eyes and practice thinking of a pleasant scene (like being at the beach, the mountains or a park) for a few minutes. You may have to help him think of a pleasant scene. Try to use one he may have actually experienced. Encourage him to be actively involved in the pleasant scene by saying, "See yourself, feel yourself in that favorite place that you have chosen. Look around and see the shapes and colors, hear the sounds. Let yourself really be there now. It's good for everybody to be in a favorite place sometimes, a place where you like to be, a place where you like how you feel. You can feel those good feelings now. Take some time to enjoy it."

2. After the child has spent some time with this activity for a few minutes, ask him to stop for a moment and check the color on the Stress Sensor Card. Hopefully it has changed to a new color that indicates he is more relaxed. Talk with your child about the experience. Ask him to share the detail of his experience with you.

If your child was successful with this exercise, then continue to use the pleasant scene to try to get the Stress Sensor Card all the way to the color blue. If your child was not successful, you may either have him try again using the same scene or try another scene. Not all children like to go to a favorite place. Below are some other mental pictures that have been successful in helping children become relaxed.

Multiple Animals. If the child likes animals, ask him to tell which one he likes best. Ask him to picture himself sitting with a puppy (or whatever animal he likes). Ask him to close his eyes and to feel the puppy's soft fur and see its color. He can have the puppy be any color and type he wants. He can also have more than one puppy. He can sit and pet the puppy or play with the puppy.

Favorite Activity. Ask the child what he likes to do. Then say, "Imagine that you can see yourself doing that. Let yourself really enjoy it." Some possibilities could be playing a musical instrument, riding a bike, riding a horse, playing on the swing or slide at the playground, or playing a video game.

Cloud Gazing. "What are some colors you like? Good. Let yourself imagine some beautiful clouds in the sky and see them change into one of your favorite colors. Good. Now let them change into another color or perhaps several nice colors. The clouds may change shape too, as you continue to watch them. It will be interesting to see what they become. You can be part of those clouds, if you like, feeling very comfortable, very good."

Favorite Song. "I know you like to sing. Where do you like to do that best? Good. Imagine that you are there now, singing your favorite song. Sing the song through in your mind. Enjoy doing it very well, making just the sounds you like."

Listening to Music. "I know you like listening to music. What is your favorite song? Just imagine yourself hearing that very clearly now, as loud or soft as you like. You may imagine watching the musicians too." You may even let your child listen to a CD at first and then later hear it in his mind.

Sports Activity. "I know you like to play football. Imagine yourself at the age you are now or older, playing on your favorite football team, wearing its uniform, playing the position you like. Let yourself get very comfortable as you imagine a game with your team winning. You are helping your team win. Feel your control as your muscles move the way you tell them, running or throwing or kicking. Enjoy being with the winning team, and continue until the game is won."

3. Set aside a time to practice this on a daily basis using the Stress Sensor Card. Encourage the child to practice on his own without the Stress Sensor Card as well.

4. After he has been able to achieve a high state of relaxation using this technique, ask him to get relaxed quickly using whatever technique works best for him. Then say, "Now I want you to try to stay as relaxed as you are right now while you imagine yourself in your room at school. I want you to imagine yourself listening to the teacher. Because you are relaxed, you are able to hear and remember everything he or she says." Give him time to try this for a few minutes. Then check the Stress Sensor Card. It should continue to indicate he is relaxed. If not, ask him to use his relaxation technique and then try it again. After he is able to achieve success with this exercise, repeat it, but this time say, "Now I want you to imagine you are in your school room doing your seat work. You are able to pay attention to your work and you are able to do it well."

5. Have your child repeat step four without the use of the Stress Sensor Card. While temperature feedback is a useful technique to help a person learn to relax and reduce symptoms (in the case of ADHD such as poor attention, concentration and impulse control), the ultimate goal is to be able to achieve success without the use of the card.

Recording Progress

It is important to keep track of progress. Use the Relaxation Training Progress Chart at the end of this chapter to record progress. You should record the date of the session, the mental picture used and the maximum state of relaxation achieved by circling S for Stressed, T for Tense, C for Calm and R for Relaxed. You may also use the Relaxation Training Progress Graph by circling the diamond that goes along with the session number and state of relaxation.

Other Applications For Relaxation Training

Homework. If your child has difficulty focusing during homework sessions, have him check the Stress Sensor Card every five minutes during the homework session. As he is doing his homework, he can check the color of the Stress Sensor Card. If he sees a change in color indicating that he is less relaxed and focused, he should be instructed to take a quick "relaxation break" and practice his relaxation technique along with the mental pictures related to task completion in step four.

Sports. Children are often surprised to know that top athletes use relaxation training, including mental pictures, to improve their performance. If your child is engaged in a sport, encourage him to use this technique to help him improve. Modify step four to use mental pictures related to his sport. (For baseball, it might be for him to keep his eye on the ball and to begin his swing of the bat when the ball crosses a certain point, such as leaving the grass on the diamond). Tennis players can use mental pictures of always knowing where the ball is and being able to connect the racket with the ball at just the right time as well as being able to aim the ball at just the right spot in their opponent's court. The technique can help in any sport with a little creativity in using the right mental picture.

TOTAL FOCUS

PROGRESS CHART

Chart **1 of 2**

	Date	Mental Picture	State
1			T N C R
2			T N C R
3			T N C R
4			T N C R
5			T N C R
6			T N C R
7			T N C R
8			T N C R
9			T N C R
10			T N C R
11			T N C R
12			T N C R
13			T N C R
14			T N C R
15			T N C R
16			T N C R
17			T N C R

"State" refers to how relaxed the child seems after the exercise.
T = Tense **N** = Nervous **C** = Calm **R** = Relaxed

	Date	Mental Picture	State			
18			T	N	C	R
19			T	N	C	R
20			T	N	C	R
21			T	N	C	R
22			T	N	C	R
23			T	N	C	R
24			T	N	C	R
25			T	N	C	R
26			T	N	C	R
27			T	N	C	R
28			T	N	C	R
29			T	N	C	R
30			T	N	C	R
31			T	N	C	R
32			T	N	C	R
33			T	N	C	R
34			T	N	C	R

TOTAL FOCUS

PROGRESS CHART

Chart **2 of 2**

"State" refers to how relaxed the child seems after the exercise.
T = Tense **N** = Nervous **C** = Calm **R** = Relaxed

TOTAL FOCUS

PROGRESS GRAPH

Session	Tense	Nervous	Calm	Relaxed
1	✦	✦	✦	✦
2	✦	✦	✦	✦
3	✦	✦	✦	✦
4	✦	✦	✦	✦
5	✦	✦	✦	✦
6	✦	✦	✦	✦
7	✦	✦	✦	✦
8	✦	✦	✦	✦
9	✦	✦	✦	✦
10	✦	✦	✦	✦
11	✦	✦	✦	✦
12	✦	✦	✦	✦
13	✦	✦	✦	✦
14	✦	✦	✦	✦
15	✦	✦	✦	✦
16	✦	✦	✦	✦
17	✦	✦	✦	✦
18	✦	✦	✦	✦
19	✦	✦	✦	✦
20	✦	✦	✦	✦
21	✦	✦	✦	✦
22	✦	✦	✦	✦
23	✦	✦	✦	✦
24	✦	✦	✦	✦
25	✦	✦	✦	✦
26	✦	✦	✦	✦
27	✦	✦	✦	✦
28	✦	✦	✦	✦
29	✦	✦	✦	✦
30	✦	✦	✦	✦

In Focus

- Stress is the body's adaptive response to fear. When your child uses the relaxation exercises in Total Focus, he is learning to trigger the "relaxation response" that allows his body to return to a normal, calm state.

- As a parent, using the relaxation exercises will allow you to think more clearly in everyday parenting situations and respond to parenting challenges more calmly.

- Biofeedback is a procedure that provides information about a body function. In Total Focus, we use a type of biofeedback called temperature biofeedback.

- Use the Stress Sensor Card and Stress Sensor Dots to help your child monitor his stress and frustration level. They can be used as a signal to take a break and practice his relaxation exercises. This can help to reduce hyperactivity and promote better impulse control and self-control.

What's Next?

ADHD kids often need extra help in learning the fine art of how to win friends and influence people. They have difficulty picking up on social cues. They don't always know when they have lost their audience for their comedy, and they tend to over-react emotionally to negative social interactions. Parents can help by demonstrating appropriate social skills and by teaching them to their child. Total Focus has several valuable tools to help your child improve his ability to get along with others at home, at school, and in the community.

Have your child listen to the tracks on Children's Audio B called *Problem Solving Made Easy* and *Secrets of Making Friends*. Companion materials for these lessons are found in the workbook, immediately following this chapter. You can tear out the sheets for your child, to help remind him of what he learned in these lessons.

You'll also find two more helpful tools: Social Skills Rules and the Feeling Faces Chart. Instructions for parents are provided with each of these tools.

When you're ready, please continue with Parent's Lesson Four in the workbook. Lesson Four will help you get better behavior and cooperation from your child at home.

TOTAL FOCUS

PROBLEM SOLVING MADE EASY

"To solve a problem, we look for an IDEA that works."
- Dr. Bob

IDEA

Identify the problem. What's happening that I don't like?

Decide what I can do about the problem. Brainstorm different things to do.

Evaluate the choices. Pick the best one.

Action. What do I need to do to solve the problem?

MAKING FRIENDS

"To make friends, you need to be a friend." - *Dr. Bob*

FRIEND

Fun. It's all about fun.

Relax. Don't get uptight. Be cool.

Invite. The best way to make a friend is to invite them to do something. Talk to your parents about it.

Encourage. Use encouraging words. Give compliments. Give warm fuzzies, not cold pricklies.

Nice Attitude. Be easygoing, relaxed, and polite.

Do kind things. Friends help their friends and do kind things for them.

Social Skills Rules

This helpful tool breaks down important social skills into simple components or "rules." This approach to teaching social skills has been found to be very successful with ADHD kids. It gives them specific behaviors to exhibit in a given type of social interaction and a sequence of how and when they should be woven into a social exchange. Here are the basic steps for teaching social skills to children:

1. Select one social skill at a time and continue with instruction and positive reinforcement of the skill until it is well established in your child's social repertoire.

2. Review the rules with your child. You can make a poster with the rules and perhaps a picture that illustrates the skill.

3. With young children, you can practice the skill through role play. This can involve you and your child taking each side of the exchange. Another fun way is to use puppets or stuffed animals to act out the scene. You can make it more fun by first demonstrating (exaggerating) the wrong way to interact in a given social situation. Then have your child tell the puppets how they should behave. Then demonstrate several times the correct way to interact using all of the "rules" and labeling each one as you go through the scenario.

4. After the demonstration and practice session, help your child to name real life situations where he can use the skill.

5. During the week, review the rules at least once a day. Your child should eventually be able to recall them from memory.

6. Look for opportunities around the home and out in the community to catch your child being good at the skill. Use descriptive praise. Point out exactly what he did and said that made the interaction a success.

7. During the week, ask your child if he had an opportunity to practice the skill at school or at play. If so, ask him to tell you about the situation. Ask him to tell you how the others reacted. Ask your child how he felt about the situation. Praise him for remembering and practicing the skill.

TOTAL FOCUS Social Skills Rules

How to Make Friends and Get Along with Others
You **CAN** get along with others and make lots of friends by practicing these social skills

LISTENING	HAVING A CONVERSATION	SAYING THANK YOU
Use good eye contact Be quiet Show you're listening (nod head, etc.) Be patient	Use good eye contact Use a friendly face and voice Keep on the same subject Be a good listener Be patient – wait your turn	Choose to say thank you Think about what you say Use a friendly face and voice Say what you are thankful for
FOLLOWING DIRECTIONS	**ASKING FOR HELP**	**SHARING**
Listen carefully Use a friendly face and voice Ask questions Say what you think you are to do Do everything you were asked to do	Know what you want to ask help for Choose who you should ask for help Use a friendly face and voice Get permission to ask for help Ask slowly and wait for their answer	Choose something to share Choose who to share it with Get an OK to share from an adult Choose the best time to share Offer to share. Be able to accept a NO
GIVING A COMPLIMENT	**ACCEPTING A COMPLIMENT**	**APOLOGIZING**
Choose what you want to say Be honest Use a friendly face and voice Say what you like about the person	Stop and think, "Was that a compliment?" Think about what you should say Use a friendly face and voice Say what you are thankful for	Stop and think, "Should I apologize?" Think about what you should say Use a friendly face and voice Be honest Say "I am sorry for _____"
WAITING YOUR TURN	**INTERRUPTING A PERSON**	**SUGGESTING AN ACTIVITY**
Choose to say thank you Think about what you say Use a friendly face and voice Say what you are thankful for	Stop and think, "Is this a good time?" Choose to interrupt or wait awhile Use a friendly face and voice Say, "Excuse me." If they say it's OK – talk If they say not now, say "OK" and wait	Choose something you want to do Choose who you want do it with you Choose what to say Choose the right time to say it Say it with a friendly face and voice If the answer is "no," ask -"What would you like to do?"
PLAYING A GAME	**WINNING**	**LOSING**
Think about the rules of the game Understand the rules of the game Decide who goes first – second, etc. Wait your turn Think about how you played When the game is over, say something nice about the game.	Don't worry about winning or losing When the game is over say something nice like, "That was fun." Or "Good game." If a another player says you won, say "Thanks – I had fun." Then compliment other players: "You are a good player too."	Don't worry about winning or losing When the game is over say something nice like, "That was fun." Or "Good game." Congratulate the winner(s) Say to yourself – "I play to have fun, not to win. Sometimes I will win and sometimes I will lose but I can ALWAYS have FUN!"

Feeling Faces Chart

The chart on the next page is useful in helping children learn to identify feelings being expressed by others, as well as helping them to tell others how they are feeling. ADHD kids often do not correctly pick up on non-verbal social cues. As a result, they do not respond appropriately to the cues, which often is misinterpreted by others as indicating the child does not care about others. Many ADHD kids have difficulty sharing their feelings. When asked how they are feeling at a given moment, they may either say, "I don't know" or select from a limited sets of labels such as mad, sad, or happy that may not accurately reflect their current emotional state. There are several activities you can engage in with your child using this tool that will improve their ability to identify and express feelings.

- Cover the feeling label for each of the faces and ask your child to tell you how the person is feeling. If he gets it right, praise him. If he misses it, given him the correct answer and give some examples when this feeling may be shown in a number of real life situations.

- Go through the chart and ask your child to describe situations when he has observed someone else or when the child himself has expressed the feeling. Let him know that it is OK to have any of these feelings from time to time. Also tell him that it is important to share how he is feeling with people he can trust. On the other hand, also let him know that sometimes we can express our feelings either at the wrong time or in the wrong way, which can cause problems. So we need to know how we are feeling and how to let people know how we are feeling. Learning to do this helps in making friends and helps other people to understand how you are feeling so they can help you when you need it and share in your happiness or your being upset.

- When your child's behavior reflects strong feeling either positive or negative, ask him how he is feeling. If he can't tell you, have him use the chart to identify how he is feeling. Encourage him to use words to let others know how he is feeling.

TOTAL FOCUS — Feeling Faces Chart

AFRAID			
ANGRY			
BORED			
EMBARRASSED			
EXCITED			
HAPPY			
JEALOUS			

On Task and In Control at Home

Overview

The chief symptoms of ADHD are poor attention and concentration, poor impulse control, and hyperactivity. These symptoms can lead to problems at home as well as at school. In the home setting, poor attention and concentration lead to problems with following directions and completing chores. Poor impulse control may result in disruptive or destructive behavior. Hyperactivity may produce a child who is either constantly in motion or is always complaining that he is bored.

In this lesson, we will provide some guidelines and tools to enable parents to help their child apply the skills they have developed through the Total Focus Program to the home setting. The role of the parent should be like that of a teacher or a coach. Children need to be shown and taught appropriate behavior. They need to be encouraged to practice what they are taught, and praised and rewarded when they are successful. They also must learn to accept the consequences and take personal responsibility when they do not play by the rules or fail to carry out their tasks.

Guidelines

1. Try to set aside time on a regular basis to do something fun with your child.

2. Catch him being good. Praise him. (Tip: ADHD children respond very positively to words of encouragement. Your child will notice and respond when you use a motivational "vocabulary" with him.) Have a look at the Words of Encouragement and Praise guide on page 94 for some great suggestions on language you can use with your child to motivate him.

3. Rather than tell him what not to do, teach and show him what he should do.

4. Use descriptive praise when he does something well. Say, "I like how you listen and give me good eye contact when I'm talking to you. Thanks." "I like how you put your bike in the garage when you're done with it." "I really liked how polite you were when you were talking to Aunt Jean this afternoon. You said 'please' and 'thank you.' Good job." Be specific.

5. Help your child learn to express how he feels. Say: "You seem frustrated." "How are you feeling?" "Are you upset?" "You look like you are angry about that." "It's OK to feel that way."

6. Try to see a situation the way your child does. Listen carefully to him. Try to form a mental picture of how it would look to him.

83

7. Use a soft, confident tone of voice to redirect him when he is upset.

8. Be a good listener: Use good eye contact. (Physically get down to the level of smaller children.) Don't interrupt. Ask open ended questions. Repeat back to him what you heard.

9. See your role as that of a teacher or coach. Demonstrate in detail how you would like him to behave. Have him practice the behavior. Give him encouragement along with constructive criticism.

10. Make sure he understands directions. Have him repeat them back.

11. When possible give him choices of when and how to comply with a request.

12. Look for gradual changes in behavior. Don't expect too much. Praise behavior that is coming closer to the desired goal.

13. Develop a nonverbal sign (gesture) that your child will accept as a signal that he is being inappropriate and needs to change his behavior. (This helps him to respond to your prompt without getting upset).

TOOLS

Rewards. Whenever possible try to use reward and praise to motivate your child to improve his behavior.

You can use Grandma's Rule. Say, "When you have picked up all your clothes, you may go out and play." Be sure you use "when" rather than "if."

Combine reward with timeout for serious disruptive or defiant behaviors. Say, "Every time you _____, you will have a _____ time out. If you can go the whole (day, afternoon, etc.) without getting a timeout, you will earn X."

If you are having trouble getting your child to do something when you ask, have him become a member of The First Time Club. (For more information, please review the Total Focus Bonus CD–ADHD: First Aid for Parents.) Use the First Time Club Chart found in the bonus section of this workbook. Tell the child that each time he does something the first time he is asked, a happy face will be placed in a square. When all the squares are completed, he will earn a reward. Mutually agree on the reward. For younger children, you can place a picture of the reward on the chart. For older children, you can write it on the chart.

Then practice with the child how he is to behave. "Each time I ask you to do something, I want you to: (1) Use good eye contact, (2) listen quietly, (3) say 'OK I will _____,' then (4) do it." Practice this, making a number of requests. Then start the program. Be sure to praise him for each success during practice as well as when the program starts. By the time the squares are filled, he has developed a new habit. When he completes the program, provide the reward immediately. Take the chart down and let him have it as part of the reward. Continue to use praise and encouragement to make sure this new habit remains and becomes even stronger.

If you want your child to exhibit a behavior without a request, such as completing a specific chore, getting homework done without a fuss, exhibiting a social skill, going to bed on time, having a clean room, etc., you can use the *Super Success Chart* included in this workbook lesson. To use the chart you need to: (1) decide on a behavior to increase, (2) decide on a reward, (3) complete the chart. For younger children, you can place a circle in several squares along the way and state they can earn a smaller reward when those circles can be turned into happy faces.

If your child is having a lot of difficulty getting along at home, consider using a Token Economy. This is a very powerful tool. When used consistently, most children will show great improvement within a few weeks. The program provides immediate reward for appropriate behavior and immediate consequences for inappropriate behavior. By the way, if you have other children around the same age as the child for whom you are designing this program, put them on the program as well. Children really like this system. Parents love the system. You can use a point chart to keep an accounting of points earned, lost, and spent. See the sample chart we have provided on page 89. For younger children, you can make it more understandable and perhaps more fun using play money or poker chips. If you use something tangible, you will need a "bank" in which to store the tokens and have them ready for use. Then use an envelope or a paper cup for the child to use as a "wallet" or "piggy bank." When you use real tokens, you should also use the chart so you have a record of your progress.

Here are the steps to follow to use this program with your child:

1. Hold a family meeting to discuss the need for the program. Tell him that it will help him to learn to be in charge of himself. You can tell older children that this system is similar to what adults experience: (1) Adults earn money for working. (2) Adults have to pay fines for breaking rules like speeding or making a late payment. (3) Adults spend their money on things they need as well as a few things they want.

2. Develop a list of behaviors for which he will earn points. Start with the morning and then go throughout the day looking for behaviors to reward. These can include positive attitude, self-help behaviors and chores. Since you are already using the behavior modification program for school, you can give him credit for each point earned on that system. Some possibilities are: getting up on time, brushing teeth, getting ready for school on time, playing nicely with a brother or sister, completing chores such as feeding a pet or taking out the trash, saying please and thank you, doing things the first time he is asked, doing homework without a fuss, getting ready for bed on time, going to bed on time, and cleaning his bedroom.

3. Agree on a list of behaviors that result in a loss of points. These can include behaviors that are oppositional, defiant, or disruptive. Some examples are: tantrums, yelling, screaming, fighting, arguing, throwing things, jumping on the furniture, getting up after bedtime, swearing, and putting others down. (More serious behaviors will receive a timeout as well as a fine).

4. Agree on a list of privileges he will earn and pay for with points. Some privileges will be bought for the day; others will be bought for a period of time (usually a half hour). These can include: watching TV, playing outside, computer time, bike riding, playing a game with a parent, etc.

5. Assign point values to each item on the list. See the sample below:

EARN POINTS FOR	Making bed	2
	Picking up bedroom	2
	Brushing teeth	2
	Setting the table	4
	Ready for bed on time	2
	Going to bed on time	2
	Doing things the first time asked	1
	Saying please and thank you	1

LOSE POINTS FOR	Throwing things	4 +Timeout
	Tantrums	4
	Arguing	2
	Interrupting	2
	Running in the house	2

PRIVILEGES TO SPEND POINTS FOR	Playing outside	5 points
	Riding bike	5 points for the day
	Going to friends	10 points
	Playing game with parent	5 points

6. Post the list of behaviors and points earned or lost in a convenient place.

7. Start using the program. Feel free to modify the program at any time by holding a meeting. Sometimes point values need to be raised or lowered to achieve a goal. You may add or remove items from the list as well.

8. After about six weeks, you may be able to start short trials off the system. Say, "Today we are going to try not using the chip system. If things go well we will try it again the next day." If the trial is successful, continue for about a week. If things continue to go well, hold a meeting and celebrate all that you and your child have both gained from the system. If your child is not ready, continue with the program.

9. Note: If your child runs out of points, have a list of extra chores they can do to earn points so that they remain on the system.

TOTAL FOCUS Super Success Chart

_____ wants to be successful at _____
Each time he/she is successful a _____ will be put in a square. When all the squares are full
he/she will earn _____ for being a SUPER SUCCESS.

TOTAL FOCUS

TOKEN ECONOMY CHART

Name: _____

Week of: ___/___ to ___/___

Earn Points For:	Points	M	T	W	T	F	S	S
Total Earned								
Carry Over From Day Before								
Lose Points For:								
Total Lost								
Net Points								
Spending:								
Points Left								
Carry Over To Next Day								

TIMEOUT

Purpose of Timeout. Timeout means time out from positive reinforcement. It is a procedure used to decrease undesirable behaviors. The main principle of this procedure is to ensure that the individual in timeout is not able to receive any reinforcement for a particular period of time.

Timeout Area. The timeout area should be easily accessible, and in such a location that the child can be easily monitored while in timeout. For example, if most activity takes place on the first floor of the house, then the timeout area should not be on an upper floor. A chair in the corner of the dining room is an excellent spot. Placing a kitchen timer on the table is a good way to keep the child informed of how much time he has left to serve.

Amount of Time Spent in Timeout. Generally, it is considered more effective to have short periods of timeout. For example, five to ten minutes is more effective than a long period, such as half an hour to an hour. Children can fairly quickly begin to use their imagination to turn a boring activity into an interesting one. Children from two to five years old should receive a two- to five-minute timeout. A six-year-old child should probably receive about a five-minute timeout. A ten-year-old child, a ten-minute timeout. (Note: ADHD children may benefit from shorter times than those suggested above). For children over ten years of age, see "Alternatives To Time Out" later in this lesson of the workbook.

Specifying Target Behaviors. You should select only ONE behavior for timeout. This will better enable the child to associate the consequence with the behavior. Select the behavior that is the most dangerous or detrimental. When this behavior has been eliminated, you then move on to another if necessary.

It is very important that the child be aware of the behaviors that are targeted for reduction. The behaviors should be very concretely defined. For example, hitting means striking someone else with the hand or an object, or coming home late means arriving home any time after 5:00pm.

Procedures for Timeout

- When a child is told to go into timeout, a parent should only say, "You have a timeout for _____" and state the particular offense. There should be no further discussion.

- Use a kitchen timer with a bell. Set the timer for the length of the timeout and tell the child he must stay in timeout until the bell rings.

- While in timeout, the child should not be permitted to talk, and the parent should not communicate with the child in any way. The child also should not make noises in any way, such as mumbling or grumbling. He should not be allowed to play with any toy, to listen to the radio or stereo, watch television, or bang on the furniture. Any violation of timeout should result in automatic resetting of the clock for another timeout period.

- It is important that all members of the household be acquainted with the regulations for timeout, so that they will not interfere with the child in timeout in any way, for example, by turning on the radio.

Strategies for Handling Refusal or Resistance

While timeout works well, it can only work when the child actually serves the timeout. There are a number of ways to handle refusal. None of them will work for all children. You may have to experiment to determine which one will work for your child.

- Tell younger children that you will count to three, and if they are not in timeout when you get to three, the timeout will be doubled.

- Children with severe ADHD or Oppositional Defiant Disorder may need to be placed on a short reward program. This could include a chart with 20 to 30 squares. Each time a child does a timeout, the child gets a star or sticker on the chart. When the chart is full, they can earn a special treat for learning how to do timeout.

- Use response cost. Select an activity or object you can take away. Tell the child that until he does the timeout, he will not be able to use the object or engage in the activity. For instance, you can unplug the TV and tell him that he may not watch TV or play a video game until he does the timeout.

Advantage of Timeout

- It is less aversive than other procedures, such as physical punishment.

- It eliminates a lot of yelling and screaming on the part of the parents.

- It increases the probability that parents are going to be consistent about what is going to be punished, when, and how.

- The child learns to accept his own responsibility for undesirable behavior. The parents are not punishing the child; rather the child is punishing himself. The child should be repeatedly told that the parents did not put him in timeout, but that the child put himself in timeout.

- The child more readily learns to discriminate which behaviors are acceptable and which are unacceptable.

- The child begins to learn more self-control.

- By keeping a written record of timeouts, parents can see if the procedure is reducing the targeted behavior. Also, reward can be tied to only receiving a certain amount of timeouts in a day or a smaller time period.

Alternatives to Timeout

Children age ten and over may decide they are "too big" for timeout because "it's for babies." Here are some other negative consequences that have been successful in reducing inappropriate behavior.

Tell the child that each time he displays the inappropriate behavior, he will have to write sentences to remind him of how he should behave. For instance, "Every time you talk back, you will have to write, 'I will talk nicely and show respect to my parents.'" The first time this happens on a given day, the sentence is written five times. If this does not help him remember, then the next time the sentence is written ten times. The number is increased by five or doubled (depending on the age of the child) each time the behavior occurs on that day. The next day the first occurrence receives five sentences.

Remove privileges or objects that you can control. Make a list of privileges or objects (TV, ride bike, stay up late, go outside and play, etc.). Tell the child that each time the undesirable behavior occurs, one item will be crossed of the list for that day. Each day the procedure starts over.

Follow the "3 Fs" of Positive Parenting

DISCIPLINE SHOULD BE:

Firm: Consequences should be clearly stated and then adhered to when the inappropriate behavior occurs.

Fair: The punishment should fit the crime. Also, in the case of recurring behavior, consequences should be stated in advance so the child knows what to expect. Harsh punishment is not necessary. Using a simple timeout can be effective when it is used consistently every time the behavior occurs. Also, give a reward for a period of time like part of a day or a whole day when no timeouts or maybe only one timeout has occurred.

Friendly: Use a friendly but firm communication style when letting a child know he has behaved inappropriately, and let him know he will receive the "agreed upon" consequence. Encourage him to try to remember what he should do instead to avoid future consequences. Work at "catching him being good" and praise him for appropriate behavior.

WORDS OF ENCOURAGEMENT AND PRAISE

Children with ADHD thrive on positive attention. Like all children, they need to feel loved and appreciated. Most parents find that it is easier to provide negative feedback rather than positive feedback. By selecting and using some of the phrases on the next page on a daily basis with your child, you will find that he will start paying more attention to you and will try harder to please. Recent research shows that ADHD children may need more praise than the average child. Unfortunately, because of their behavior, they often receive less.

WORDS OF ENCOURAGEMENT AND PRAISE

yes	good	fine
very good	very fine	excellent
marvelous	at-a-boy	right
that's right	correct	wonderful
I like the way you do that	I'm pleased with (proud of) you	that's good
wow	oh boy	very nice
good work	great going	good for you
that's the way	much better	OK
you're doing better	that's perfect	good idea
what a clever idea	that's it	good job
great job controlling yourself	I like the way you _____	I noticed that you _____
keep it up	I had fun _____ with you	you are improving at _____more and more
you showed a lot of responsibility when you _____	way to go	I appreciate the way you ___
you are great at that	you're the best	good remembering
I like the way you___ without having to be asked (reminded)	that's beautiful	I'm sure glad you are my son/daughter
now you've got it	I like your_____	I love you

You can show them how you feel as well as tell them.

- Smile
- Nod
- Pat on shoulder, head, knee
- Wink
- Signal or gesture to signify approval

- High five
- Touch cheek
- Tickle
- Laugh (with, not at)
- Pat on the back, hug

A Personal Tip from Dr. Bob
The Special 20

This is a recommendation I would make to any parent with any kind of child, but it's especially important for ADHD kids. When parents would come to see me, after the first meeting or two, I would tell them that I have a prescription that can fix a lot of the problems with their children.

Attempt to spend twenty minutes a day, either as a group or individually, with each child in your family.

Often when I would give this prescription, parents would wonder how it could ever work. They'd say, "Well, but I come home late. We have soccer practice. I have work to do at night." And I'd say, "You know, I understand all of that. But, does your child understand that?" I'm not saying the reason these parents came to see me was because they weren't spending enough time with their kids, because that's not true. And I'm not saying that about you, either. They cared enough about their kids to come to see me, and you care enough about your child to use the Total Focus Program. So it's not a matter of caring. It's really just a matter of understanding one very basic fact about children. We as parents have to remember that kids don't choose to be born. We as parents choose to have them. And for good reason. We want to be parents. We want to have kids. We want to love another individual. But today we're under multiple pressures. In many families, both parents have to work—sometimes a full-time and a part-time job each. And, for a lot of us, work doesn't stop at 40 hours. I see people in the mall, even at church, busy answering emails on their blackberry or their cell phones. A lot of us are working 24/7. And you need time for yourself, certainly.

None of those are bad things. But as a child psychologist and as a parent, I think we have to get our priorities straight. The most important thing we can do as parents is to spend time with a child in a way that's positive. No matter how they frustrate us, they still need to know that we love them. And there's an easy way to do it. Simply by playing a game for fifteen or twenty minutes. This is a prescription that will not only help your child, but if you really carry it out, it will help you. I've had many parents who resisted initially because they thought they could never find twenty minutes a day with their kids. Later they came back to me and thanked me for this. Because spending fifteen or twenty minutes a day with your kid, or all of your kids, playing, talking, having fun, turns out to be a tremendous stress reducer for parents. When you decide, "I'm going to do this, and it's not only for my kids but for me. I'm really going to get into this and have fun. I'm going to get back to the child within me and play," you not only build your child's self-esteem, but you've done things to improve your own mental and physical well-being.

I think it's good to have family time, but there still needs to be time when each parent spends one-on-one time with each child. This means dads with sons, dads with daughters. Moms with daughters, moms with sons. One-to-one. Because it's during that one-to-one time, like just riding around in the car on a Saturday doing errands, that you have the opportunity for openness where the child knows that they have your attention and they may open up and share things. It's a time when you can say special things to that child, knowing that you're not going to be saying it in front of a sibling who might be somewhat jealous if they heard it. You will find that you probably will have a somewhat different approach for each child because each child is different and each child is special.

Family time, even if it's for a few minutes a day at the dinner table, can be as simple as going around the table and having each person, adults and children, simply say what went well for them today. What was the best thing that happened to you today and what was one thing that didn't go so well for you today? That opens up an opportunity for discussion. It's been shown that mealtime together with young children and adolescents improves their self-esteem, their school achievement and lessens the likelihood that they're going to get involved in substance abuse. And guess what? It's fun. It's a time for parents to share things with each other that they might have not shared in another context.

Play a quick family game. You can play a game like Uno that lasts fifteen or twenty minutes where everybody can have fun. Play board games. In good weather you can go out and play catch. A quick game of horseshoes. Whatever. I know you spend time helping your kids with homework, going to their soccer games, going to parent conferences, taking them to the doctor, and all those things are important. But they aren't the same as that one-on-one or group time that's simply spent having fun, enjoying each other and sharing love with each other. The Special Twenty. Give it a try. Keep it going as long as your kids are around. You'll be glad you did. And so will your kids.

In Focus

- You can use a simple, reward-based behavior modification system to change your child's behavior at home.

- The Token Economy System shows the child that appropriate behavior earns him privileges around the home. Inappropriate behavior results in the loss of those privileges. Establishing this token economy at home with your child is an easy way to shape his behavior in a better direction. It also lays a foundation for what he will experience in the work world when he grows up.

- A timeout removes a child from over-stimulation or the reinforcement of an undesirable behavior. It is not in and of itself a punishment. But it is often all that is needed to correct an inappropriate behavior.

- Timeouts allow parents to be more consistent with their discipline. They give parents an alternative to screaming and arguing with the child.

- When he receives a timeout, the child gets the message that he is punishing himself.

- Keep discipline firm, fair, and friendly.

What's Next?

Listen to the track on Children's Audio B called *I CAN at Home* with your child. We provide a companion reminder sheet for this lesson on page 99, along with an I Can Club Pledge your child can use to focus him on appropriate behavior at home. You will also find Positive Self-Talk Cards on page 101. These are tools you can give your child now to help him stop his negative "stinking thinking" at school and at home. They will also help change his thinking to encourage more positive, cooperative behavior with family members.

I Can Club Pledge

I pledge to myself and my family that I will:

Have an "I Can" attitude

Be helpful to others

Say positive things to others

Do my best at everything I try

Follow directions from my parents and teachers

Stop and think before I do things

Honestly share my thoughts and feelings

Stay positive when things don't go my way

Say this pledge to myself every day!

HOME

Helper Attitude. Always look for ways to help. When asked to help out, be cheerful.

Own Your Own Stuff. Admit your mistakes. Use "I Messages," not "You Messages."

Mind Your Own Business. Respect everyone. Give people quiet time when they need it. Don't be a tattletale.

Enjoy Your Family. Give warm fuzzies, not cold pricklies.

100

TOTAL FOCUS

I CAN ask questions when I need help.

TOTAL FOCUS

I CAN be positive at all times.

TOTAL FOCUS

I CAN be helpful to others.

TOTAL FOCUS

I CAN say NO to things that are wrong.

TOTAL FOCUS

I CAN be a good listener.

TOTAL FOCUS

I CAN be a good follower.

TOTAL FOCUS

I CAN be a good leader.

TOTAL FOCUS

I CAN try my best always.

TOTAL FOCUS

I CAN forgive others.

TOTAL FOCUS

I CAN say kind things to others.

TOTAL FOCUS

I CAN learn something new each day.

TOTAL FOCUS

I CAN have fun and feel good about life.

Learning to Slow Down and Think:

Improving Self-Control

Overview

Children with ADHD often have difficulty sitting still. They also have difficulty exercising self-control. These two conditions are usually what cause a child with ADHD to be singled out for special attention by a teacher. Children with poor attention and concentration will have poor academic achievement and may eventually come to the attention of a teacher. You can be sure that a child who is causing disruption in the classroom will soon prompt a parent conference.

This portion of the program uses two psychological methods to help your child improve self-control: relaxation training and cognitive rehabilitation training or brain training. The exercises in this section are based on these two methods and will give your child practice in developing his ability to control his activity level and learning to think and anticipate consequences before he acts. The exercises will continue to improve his ability to relax, while also adding mental coping statements that will help him to sit still, stay on task, and "stop and think" before acting.

Research has shown that cognitive rehabilitation training can help children learn basic cognitive skills. These skills come naturally to most children, but seem to be difficult for ADHD children to learn. Through conscious controlled effort and repetitive practice, ADHD children can learn these skills. While they will need to work hard at first to develop the skills, they will eventually become automatic with continued practice.

This component of Total Focus uses the same type of mental pictures used in the relaxation training component as a conscious effort to attain a state of total relaxation. Specific suggestions of mental pictures are also given to enable the child to use appropriate coping strategies to direct his day-to-day activities in a positive way. So often children and adults allow negative mental pictures to occupy their mind, which results in inappropriate responses to daily life situations. The popular motivational speaker, Zig Ziglar, has helped thousands of people, including children and adults, to learn to change the mental pictures they have stored in their mind from ones that are self-destructive to ones that promote positive achievement. He rightly points out that this is only taking a natural process and using it in a positive way. He states that this is not mind control or related to secular humanism, but rather it is taking positive action to renew our minds.

The Children's Audio Lesson for this portion of Total Focus is called *Learning to Slow Down and Think*. It contains a number of positive mental pictures. In order for you to encourage your child to remember and use these pictures, I suggest you listen to the lesson with your child at least once. Then remind him to use these images when they would be helpful.

HOW TO USE THESE TECHNIQUES

1. Have your child listen to the track on Children's Audio C called *Learning to Slow Down and Think*. Another for children age 10 and over. Choose the lesson that best suits your child's developmental level. The first time he listens to the lesson, you should listen along with him. He may feel silly at first, but encourage him to continue to listen. Remind him that his mind works like a computer, and by listening to the CD, he is adding a "new program" to his mind that will help him improve his learning ability. Let him know that some top athletes use this method to improve their performance. For the first week, have your child listen to the CD every other day. For the next nine weeks, have him listen to the CD every three days. Some children find that a good time to listen is right before they go to bed. The relaxing quality of the lesson often helps them to get right to sleep.

2. Practice each of the exercises in this workbook lesson daily (I suggest five times per week) for two weeks. Keep track of your child's progress on the chart provided with each exercise. You will find the exercises here in the workbook on cards that are conveniently perforated so you can tear them out. A good time to do these exercises is in the afternoon or evening before doing homework. Let your child know that these exercises are similar to those used in karate and other programs to improve self-control. These exercises help to strengthen his mind and will help him at school as well as in sports and other activities.

    (Feel free to modify the instructions to be more appropriate for the age of your child. Not all children will want to do all the exercises. Try to encourage them to complete them all. Most younger children can perform all of them. Older children may think they are silly, but you can tell them that adults practice similar exercises to improve performance for various athletic or artistic activities.)

EXERCISE 1

TOTAL FOCUS

Purpose: The purpose of this exercise is to help the child to learn deep breathing, which improves his ability to relax.

Materials: A kitchen timer with a bell, a kitchen chair, a book, carpeted floor or a rug or mat to place on an uncarpeted floor.

Method:

1. To prepare your child for this exercise say, "I want you to lie down and put this book on your stomach. Next, I want you to slowly take in a deep breath. As you breathe in, the book should rise up. Now, slowly let the breath out. As you let the breath out, the book should go back down. Practice this until you can become good at making the book rise and fall with each breath."

2. Say to your child, "Set the timer for one minute. Sit in a chair with your feet on the floor in a comfortable position and cross your hands on your lap." When he has done that say, "Now close your eyes and breathe deeply. Try to breathe in deeply and then slowly let the breath out. Count to yourself, silently, the number of breaths you take. I will also count them for you silently. When the timer bell rings, open your eyes and write down the number of breaths you took in that one-minute period." Have the child repeat the exercise and attempt to decrease the number of breaths taken on each trial.

EXERCISE 2

TOTAL FOCUS

Purpose: The purpose of this exercise is to help the child to learn to sit quietly for increasing amounts of time. This will improve his ability to exercise self-control.

Materials: Mirror, book, stopwatch, or regular watch.

Method: Say to your child, "Start the watch (or mark the time if using a regular watch). We will start now. I want you to sit comfortably cross legged on the floor in front of the mirror. Carefully sit up straight and place a book on your head. Balance the book and watch yourself in the mirror as long as you can without moving. When you move or when the book falls, record your time." The child should continue to try this and see if he can remain perfectly still for longer periods of time.

TRIAL #	BREATHS	TRIAL #	BREATHS
1		11	
2		12	
3		13	
4		14	
5		15	
6		16	
7		17	
8		18	
9		19	
10		20	

Children should make two tries each day they practice the exercise. They should practice the exercise daily (5 times in a week) for two weeks.

TRIAL #	TIME	TRIAL #	TIME
1		11	
2		12	
3		13	
4		14	
5		15	
6		16	
7		17	
8		18	
9		19	
10		20	

Children should make two tries each day they practice the exercise. They should practice the exercise daily (5 times in a week) for two weeks.

EXERCISE 3

Purpose: The purpose of this exercise is to help the child to learn to gradually lengthen the time required to lift his leg, while lying flat on the floor. This will help him improve self-control and reduce hyperactivity.

Materials: Stopwatch or regular watch, carpeted floor, or a rug or mat to place on an uncarpeted floor.

Method: Tell your child to lie down on his back with his legs together. His arms should be at his sides, palms down. Have him start the stopwatch or mark the time he starts the exercise. Then say, "Slowly lift your right leg off the floor and raise it as far as it will go. Now slowly return it to the floor. Stop the watch and record your time." Then say, "Now slowly lift your left leg off the floor and raise it as far as it will go, and slowly return it to the floor. Stop the watch and record your time." When he has completed this say, "This time, repeat the exercise and see if you can move much more slowly than before. Be sure to record your time."

EXERCISE 4

Purpose: The purpose of this exercise is to help the child to learn to concentrate on a pendulum and hold it still for as long as possible. This improves attention and concentration while reducing hyperactivity.

Materials: Table, penny, pendulum (item such as a washer or key on a six inch string), stopwatch or regular watch.

Method: Have the child start the stopwatch or mark the time and sit down, with elbows on the table and hands folded. Then say, "Hold the end of the string above the penny, about two inches off the table. Concentrate on holding the pendulum perfectly still, without moving or touching the table or penny. When you finally move or touch the penny, record your time." Next time, tell the child you will watch him like a judge to be sure the pendulum does not move significantly from the penny or touch it in any way. He should try to increase his time.

TRIAL #	RIGHT	LEFT	TRIAL #	RIGHT	LEFT
1			11		
2			12		
3			13		
4			14		
5			15		
6			16		
7			17		
8			18		
9			19		
10			20		

Children should make two tries each day they practice the exercise. They should practice the exercise daily (5 times in a week) for two weeks.

TRIAL #	TIME	TRIAL #	TIME
1		11	
2		12	
3		13	
4		14	
5		15	
6		16	
7		17	
8		18	
9		19	
10		20	

Children should make two tries each day they practice the exercise. They should practice the exercise daily (5 times in a week) for two weeks.

EXERCISE 5

Purpose: The purpose of this exercise is to help the child to learn to sit quietly at a desk while holding a pencil. This improves attention, concentration and reduces hyperactivity.

Materials: Chair placed in front of a table or desk, pencil, stopwatch, or regular watch.

Method: Have the child start the stopwatch or mark the time and sit down. Say to him, "Sit up straight in your chair in a comfortable position. Take the pencil in one hand and place that hand on top of your other hand in the middle of the desk." Then say, "Take several deep breaths and relax your entire body. Close your eyes and concentrate on the feeling of the pencil in your hand. Keep your eyes closed, tell yourself to relax, and do not move. Be absolutely quiet and do not move any part of your body. When you finally move a part of your body, open your eyes and write down the time you finished the exercise and the total time you were able to keep still." Then say, "Now try it again, and see if you can be absolutely still for an even longer time."

TRIAL #	TIME	TRIAL #	TIME
1		11	
2		12	
3		13	
4		14	
5		15	
6		16	
7		17	
8		18	
9		19	
10		20	

Children should make two tries each day they practice the exercise. They should practice the exercise daily (5 times in a week) for two weeks.

TIPS FOR TEACHING SELF-CONTROL

1. Our goal is to get your child to connect behavior and consequences. We want him to understand, for instance, that running around in the house could lead to an accident and/or an object, person, or animal could be hurt. Blurting out answers at school could end up in having to stay after school or some other consequence. With any home behavior modification program that involves positive reinforcement, it's important to include any other kids in the home as well. This keeps the other kids from becoming resentful and keeps the ADHD child from feeling singled out or picked on. So as you work on teaching your ADHD child to stop and think before acting, make it a lesson for all the children. They will all benefit from it.

2. If you are encountering a problem with hyperactivity where the child is running around all the time, you can simply prompt him to slow down. Give him the High Sign, for example. To make it more effective, you can also add a reward for every day when you don't have to remind him to slow down.

3. Another technique would be to say, "We've asked you to slow down. We've talked about why it's important to slow down, but apparently we need some practice in being able to do that. The next time I have to tell you to slow down, you are going to stop what you're doing, go back to where you started running around, and then you're going to practice walking slowly five times from where you started to where you stopped."

4. Hyperactivity often occurs in new places, public places and social gatherings, where the increased stimuli increase the hyperactivity. Prior to going to a new place or a place where you know this may occur, review with the child the expected behavior. Go over it in detail. Ask the child to repeat what they should do. It's more important to emphasize what he should do rather than what he should not do. For instance, it could be sitting quietly in church or at some other kind of program. It could be staying with you and not running around when you're in the mall. My son, Greg, was one of those kids who used to crawl under the coat racks at Sears at the mall, and we would end up having to chase him. This was when he was about four. These kids do this because they think it's fun, and when they're running away from you, they think it's a game. They're really not being defiant. However, it's not a cool thing. When he did this at the mall, (along with another behavior which was asking me to buy him everything that he saw and not being very happy when I said no) we told him, "While we're in the mall, there are two rules. One is you need to stay right by me at all times, and, number two, you're not to ask for anything. If you can do this, when we are all through at the mall, we will go through Sears and you will get a box of popcorn." This worked very well. Occasionally I might need to remind him once about one thing or another, but for the most part, I restated the rules each time we went to the mall, and it worked great. The key is having the plan before you go, and letting the child know what the reward will be for the desired behavior.

You also may need to monitor play situations carefully. You may even decide that the child isn't necessarily ready to go to certain events. Again, we were very cautious when Greg was in kindergarten about allowing him to go to birthday parties. When he was about six or seven, I decided to give it a try. But at first, I went and stayed with him so that I could be there to help him if he had problems. Again, I stated in advance what the appropriate behavior was. I was surprised at one birthday party where he actually, without any prompting, behaved appropriately. So ADHD kids can learn and still have a great time.

5. When it comes to impulsivity and hyperactivity, sometimes these kids cannot do well anticipating events, including positive ones. I learned that quickly, again with Greg, and decided when some big event was going to happen, such as going to Disneyland, he never knew until we got to the park. Otherwise he just couldn't handle the excitement. Once he got there, he did fine. But the anticipation over the week prior would've been horrendous for everybody. You don't have to tell your child about an event two weeks in advance. Tell him that morning or even an hour before. That way, his excitement can be appropriate and justified. Not over the top.

6. Impulsivity is when a child does things without thinking. When they dash away from you in a crowd. When they blurt out answers in class. When they interrupt you. The number one thing you want to teach him is to stop and think. So that means saying, "Before you do something, I want you to stop and think about it." And it means taking it a step further. I learned this with a young boy named Austin years ago. He was about seven years old at the time. I assumed that when I told Austin to stop and think at school, that he knew what I meant. Then I discovered that we had to go further. Here's what I said to Austin: "Okay, what I mean when I ask you to stop and think before you do something at school or at home is, for instance, the next time you think about throwing a wad of paper across the room because you think it's fun, I want you to stop before you do that. And then think, 'If I were to raise my hand and ask the teacher if I could do that, what would she say?'"
And I asked him and he said, "She would say no."
I said, "If she said no, would you do it?"
He said, "No. I wouldn't."
And I said, "That's right, because you're a good guy. So from now on, it's the same at home. If you think that you want to put the cat in the toilet, what do you think would happen if you asked your mom if you could do that?" And then we went through the same scenario–a couple other things at home, a couple other things at school. He got it, and it was amazing to see how that helped him to use the "stop and think" technique after that.

7. The techniques we use for hyperactivity also work really well for impulse control. For waiting his turn, you may coach your child that he needs to stop, count to ten, and practice his relaxation. He may need to say things to himself silently like, "I can wait and I can be patient. This won't take forever." Teach him this ahead of time if you know he will be in that situation or if he's had problems at school.

Tell your child, "When you're in line or you have to wait your turn for something, for the teacher to get to you, to hand out something for work, this is what you need to do. You need to practice relaxing, either counting to ten or saying one of our coping phrases to help you get through." When he's being impulsive and arguing with you, say, "You are arguing with me. You need to stop now and think about the possible consequences." Dealing with impulsivity is also a good time to implement the High Sign Technique.

8. Sometimes it's helpful for an ADHD child to suffer the natural consequences of his behavior. For instance, not taking his homework to school can result in being embarrassed when the child doesn't have it when the teacher asks for it. Being overly demanding may mean that you decide not to answer his request. You can also use the Super Success Chart in the workbook. For the behavior, explain to your child, "When you can go a whole day without interrupting, then you will earn a star or happy face in the square."

9. Perfectionism is another problem ADHD kids often exhibit. Positive self-talk helps a lot here, such as, "I can get this if I stay with it. I need to do the best that I can, but I don't have to be perfect. If I continue to have problems, I can ask somebody to help me." Another way to improve frustration tolerance is to find activities that will be fairly easy for them that they can do and experience success. Also, ask them to verbalize their feelings. When they're verbalizing their feelings, you can teach them cognitive behavioral skills. You can identify, for instance, that they are awfulizing–saying things that make everything seem horrible–and you can then teach them to change their thoughts to more appropriate thinking. Rather than saying, "I'm no good at this," saying, "This is hard, but I can get it." Instead of saying, "I will never get this," to say, "It may take me a while, but I can figure this out." Or "I can ask for help."

10. It's important to recognize that for younger kids, a minute is a lifetime. So don't make them wait forever when you see that they're trying to get your attention. You can also have a message board where they can write down what they want to ask you so that when they get the chance, they won't worry about forgetting.

Sometimes I would tell parents that you need to provide a "wall" for the kid to bump into a few times. And they'll get tired of getting the headache and get with the program. Whether it's a time-out or losing points or privileges, it needs to be there every time the behavior occurs. And it should be combined with a reward or positive consequence for the non-occurrence of that behavior and, in fact, the occurrence of the opposite behavior. That's another important point to remember. The best way to change or eliminate a bad habit is to replace it with a good habit. By teaching the good habit, explaining why it's better than the old way of behaving, and then rewarding it every time that new habit occurs, that habit will gain strength and the old habit will lose strength.

In Focus

- Relaxation and cognitive rehabilitation training can help your child control his activity level and learn to think and anticipate consequences before acting.

- The relaxation exercises used in the audio lesson use mental pictures to help your child see himself acting with greater self-control.

- The brain training exercises teach basic cognitive skills that are difficult for ADHD children to learn without this type of training.

- The end result will be a calmer child who thinks before he speaks and acts. A child who has fewer outbursts. A child who manages his day-to-day activities more evenly. A happier child.

What's next?

You can move to the last lesson in the program when you feel your child is ready. All the parent's information for Lesson Six is contained next in the workbook.

Improving Attention and Concentration

Overview

Have your child listen to the track on Children's Audio C called *Improving Attention and Concentration*. They also often have difficulty with memory, sequencing (putting things in order) and categorization (putting things in groups). These cognitive skills are just like any other skill. Just as it is for athletic or musical skills, with practice, they can be learned. With repeated practice, these skills can continue to be improved.

This portion of the Total Focus Program also uses relaxation training and cognitive rehabilitation training, or brain training. The brain training exercises will give your child practice in developing his ability to concentrate and pay attention, along with learning or improving skills in categorization and sequencing. The Children's Audio Lesson (Improving Attention and Concentration) for this portion of the program will continue to improve his ability to relax, while also adding mental coping statements that will help him to pay attention, concentrate, complete tasks, and remember what he sees and hears.

The Children's Audio Lesson encourages conscious efforts to attain a state of total relaxation while imagining positive mental pictures. This enables children to use the power of these stored mental pictures to direct their day-to-day activities in a positive way.

HOW TO USE THESE TECHNIQUES

1. Have your child listen to the track on Children's Audio C called *Improving Attention and Concentration*. One for children up to age 10. Another for children age 10 and older. Choose the lesson that best suits your child's developmental level. The first time he listens to the CD, you should listen along with him. He may feel silly at first, but encourage him to continue to listen. Remind him that his mind works like a computer, and by listening to the CD, he is adding a "new program" to his mind that will help him improve his learning ability. Let him know that some top athletes use this method to improve their performance. For the first week, have your child listen to the CD every other day. For the next nine weeks, have him listen to the CD every three days. Some children find that a good time to listen is right before going to bed. The relaxing quality of the lesson often helps kids to get right to sleep.

2. Practice each of the exercises in this workbook lesson daily (at least five times per week) for two weeks. Keep track of your child's progress on the chart provided with each exercise. You will find the exercises here in the workbook on cards that are conveniently perforated so you can tear them out. A good time to do these exercises is in the afternoon or evening before doing homework. Let your child know that these exercises are similar to those used in special programs to improve learning ability and memory. Let him know that adults often use exercises similar to these to improve their performance at work.

(Feel free to modify the instructions to be more appropriate for the age of your child. Not all children will want to do all the exercises. Try to encourage them to complete them all. Most younger children can perform all of them.)

EXERCISE 6

TOTAL FOCUS

Purpose: The purpose of this exercise is to help the child pay close attention to objects being moved about and to remember where they are. This helps to improve attention and concentration.

Materials: Four colored glasses (Be sure you can't see through them.), M and M candies.

Method: Say to your child, "Look at this table with the four glasses turned upside-down on it. The glasses are colored and you cannot see through them. I will lift them up one at a time, so you can see that nothing is under them. Now I will place this M and M candy under this glass. Watch carefully as I begin to move the glass around. If you keep your eyes on it, you may have the M and M to eat. Now I have stopped moving it. Pick up the glass that you think has the candy under it. If you are correct, put a plus mark on your score sheet. If not correct put a minus mark." With additional trials, move the glasses more quickly and perhaps add a fifth glass.

EXERCISE 7

TOTAL FOCUS

Purpose: The purpose of this exercise is to help the child to learn to be able to quickly and accurately duplicate a coin pattern. This helps to improve memory and sequencing as well as attention and concentration.

Materials: Assorted coins, cardboard cover sheet, stopwatch, or regular watch.

Method: Give these instructions: "Look carefully at the coins arranged on this table. You see that there are three pennies and two nickels:

Now I am going to cover the coins with this cardboard. You take some of the other coins and make a pattern like mine over here on the other side of the table. Start the stopwatch or mark the time and make the pattern. When you finish, stop the watch or mark the time and remove the cardboard cover. Write down the time it took you and mark whether you were correct or incorrect with a plus or minus sign on your record sheet. If you were incorrect, try again until you get it correct." Increase the difficulty of the patterns given to the child, including pennies, nickels, dimes, quarters and half dollars. Later include sequences of paper dollars with coins.

TRIAL #	+ OR -	TRIAL #	+ OR -
1		11	
2		12	
3		13	
4		14	
5		15	
6		16	
7		17	
8		18	
9		19	
10		20	

Children should make two tries each day they practice the exercise. They should practice the exercise daily (5 times in a week) for two weeks.

TRIAL #	TIME + OR -	TRIAL #	TIME + OR -
1		11	
2		12	
3		13	
4		14	
5		15	
6		16	
7		17	
8		18	
9		19	
10		20	

Children should make two tries each day they practice the exercise. They should practice the exercise daily (5 times in a week) for two weeks.

EXERCISE 8

Purpose: The purpose of this exercise is to help the child to learn to accurately and quickly sort and match the number and picture cards in a deck of playing cards. This improves attention, concentration and categorization skills.

Materials: Stopwatch or regular watch, deck of playing cards.

Method: Say to the child, "Here is a full deck of playing cards. In just a minute start to sort the cards on this table as quickly as you can. Put the aces in one pile, the twos in another, the fives, kings and so forth each in a separate pile. Start your stopwatch or mark the time and go ahead. When you have finished sorting, stop your watch or mark the time. Now do it again and see if you shorten your time." In other sessions have him sort dominos, Uno cards, alphabet cards, number cards and basic vocabulary cards.

EXERCISE 9

Purpose: The purpose of this exercise is to help the child to learn to be able to correctly write as many different letters and numerals as possible in two minutes time. This improves attention, concentration, visual-motor coordination, memory and word retrieval skills.

Materials: Pencil, paper, kitchen timer with a bell.

Method: Tell the child that after setting the kitchen timer for two minutes, he is to take his pencil and paper and write as many different letters and numerals as he can until the bell rings. He may write them in any order he wishes but must write a different letter or numeral each time, working as fast as he can. When the bell rings, he is to count the total letters and numbers on his paper and record it on the score sheet. He should then try it again, concentrating on beating his previous record. In further sessions, he could write as many names as possible (in two minutes, then in three minutes). Ask him to continue with names of fruits, cars, baseball teams and so on. He should record his score and try to improve it.

TRIAL #	TIME	TRIAL #	TIME
1		11	
2		12	
3		13	
4		14	
5		15	
6		16	
7		17	
8		18	
9		19	
10		20	

Children should make two tries each day they practice the exercise. They should practice the exercise daily (5 times in a week) for two weeks.

TRIAL #	NUMBER CORRECT	TRIAL #	NUMBER CORRECT
1		11	
2		12	
3		13	
4		14	
5		15	
6		16	
7		17	
8		18	
9		19	
10		20	

Children should make two tries each day they practice the exercise. They should practice the exercise daily (5 times in a week) for two weeks.

EXERCISE 10

TOTAL FOCUS

Purpose: The purpose of this exercise is to help the child to learn to listen to a word and verbally arrange its letters in alphabetical order. This improves attention, concentration, auditory discrimination, memory and sequencing skills.

Materials: Word list.

Method: Explain to the child, "Here is a list of words that we are going to work on. Listen to the first one. It is 'cat.' The letters are C A T. Now, to begin with, you look at the word and rearrange the letters in alphabetical order and tell me what they are. For example, C A T rearranged alphabetically is A C T. Now, you say it." The child responds, "A C T." Then respond with, "Good, mark a plus on your score card next to the word 'cat.' Now rearrange the letter in these words alphabetically and mark a plus if you are correct and a minus if you are not correct." Give a list of words such as play, love, and game.

After the child finishes a simple word list, have him make up a list of his own. Then proceed to giving the words to him verbally, without him looking at a list. Ask the child to suggest his own words and sequence without visual cues. As his attention and memory develop, move on to longer and more abstract words.

WORDS	+ OR -	WORDS	+ OR -
CAT			
FUN			
LIKE			
SCHOOL			
MOVIE			
TRUCK			
SEASON			
WEDDING			

Children should make at least two tries each day they practice the exercise.
They should practice the exercise daily (5 times in a week) for two weeks.

122

ADDITIONAL ATTENTION AND CONCENTRATION EXERCISES

1. Have your child listen to story tapes with his eyes closed. After the tape is over, ask him to record on a blank tape his version of the story. Then listen together to the two tapes. Discuss how much alike the two tapes are. If he is close, a plus would be earned for the exercise. If he is not very close, a minus would be awarded.

2. Have your child quickly copy a simple Tinker Toy model. You could also use Legos, Lincoln Logs or other building materials that provide diagrams on how to build specific items. Time how long it took. Repeat to improve time. Increase the complexity of the models. This is also a good opportunity to practice handling frustration using "positive self-talk" and relaxation.

3. Lay out 16 two-inch diameter black circles on the floor. Make up a set of ten or more cards showing dot to dot patterns. Have the child look at the card and then attempt to walk the pattern following the lines connecting the dots on the card. Have him repeat by memory. Use increasingly complicated patterns. Also time how long it takes to walk a pattern and work on doing it faster on each trial.

4. Collect a set of pictures from magazines that have more and more detail in order to gradually increase the difficulty. Have the child look carefully at the picture for a minute. Have him tell you or write down everything he saw in the picture. Keep track of how many items he was able to remember.

5. Tape a series of directions such as writing letters or numbers, drawing objects, etc. Have him listen to the tape and then attempt to follow the directions. Make the directions more complicated as he progresses.

ADDITIONAL ACTIVITIES

- Crossword Puzzles–Improve attention for words and sequencing ability.

- Picture Puzzles–The child has to look for things that are wrong in the picture or look for hard-to-find objects. Trains attention and concentration.

- Mazes–These teach planning ahead and impulse control.

GAMES THAT HELP IMPROVE ATTENTION AND CONCENTRATION

- *Simon Says* This classic childhood game is the original listen-and-pay attention game.

- *Champion Distractor* One person has to focus on completing some task, while the person playing Distractor does everything possible to distract the other person and disrupt the task. In order to win, a person must work hard to be a good Distractor and also work hard at not being distracted by the other Distractors!

- **Radar Focus** The person playing the role of the radar operator has to zoom in on the person who is talking, and maintain radar focus until the person finishes talking. A good job by the radar operator is, of course, rewarded with praise and a prize.

- **Classic Games** These games can be purchased at any toy or department store and are great for family fun, but also help improve attention, concentration, executive functioning, and memory.

    - *Checkers*
    - *Concentration*
    - *Uno*

COMPUTER GAMES AVAILABLE ON THE INTERNET

- **The Kidz Page** This is a great resource. There are many games available for kids to play online. Categories that are especially helpful are: Memory Games – Strategy Brain Games – Online Puzzle Games – Learning Games. In addition to the online games, there are also printable games you can download and print out. All of the materials on the site are FREE
  http://www.thekidzpage.com/freekidsgames/index.htm

- **Aba Soft** This site has a whole library of "Flash" games for children that can be played online or downloaded to your computer. They are FREE and include the following categories: Math – Alphabet – Find the Object – Logic and Memory.
  http://www.ababasoft.com/kids/index.html

In Focus

- Relaxation and cognitive rehabilitation training can help your child improve attention span, concentration and memory.

- The relaxation exercises used in the audio lesson use mental pictures to help your child see himself concentrating and remembering what he reads and hears in class.

- The brain training exercises teach basic cognitive skills that are difficult for ADHD children to learn without this type of training—concentration, memory sequencing, executive functioning.

- The end result will be a child who is able to focus on class work and homework. A child who is more comfortable with reading. A child who can complete assignments and be successful in school...and in life.

What's Next?

Success! You and your child now have the tools you need to ensure success at home and at school, even with ADHD. Plan a celebration for completing the program. A graduation treat or dinner. And remember that while your child may graduate from the program, he will want to use the techniques learned here every day and revisit the program often for refreshers on how to improve concentration, attention and self-control. The Total Focus Program is a coaching program for life. Come back often. Come back to move forward and succeed. Congratulations!

TOTAL FOCUS Behavior Checklist

For each item, check the column which best describes this child:	Not at All (0)	Just a Little (1)	Quite a Bit (2)	Very Much (3)	Score
1. Often fails to give close attention to details or makes careless mistakes in schoolwork or tasks					
2. Often has difficulty sustaining attention in tasks or play activities					
3. Often does not seem to listen when spoken to directly					
4. Often does not follow through on instructions and fails to finish schoolwork, chores, or duties					
5. Often has difficulty organizing tasks and activities					
6. Often avoids, dislikes, or reluctantly engages in tasks requiring sustained mental effort					
7. Often loses things necessary for activities (e.g., toys, school assignments, pencils, or books)					
8. Often is distracted by outside stimuli					
9. Often is forgetful in daily activities					
10. Often has difficulty maintaining alertness, orienting to requests, or executing directions					
A - TOTAL SCORE (Attention/Concentration)					
11. Often fidgets with hands or feet or squirms in seat					
12. Often leaves seat in classroom or in other situations in which remaining seated is expected					
13. Often runs about or climbs excessively in situations in which remaining seated is expected					
14. Often has difficulty playing or engaging in leisure activities quietly					
15. Often is "on the go" or often acts as if "driven by a motor"					
16. Often talks excessively					
17. Often blurts out answers before questions have been completed					
18. Often has difficulty awaiting turn					
19. Often interrupts or intrudes on others (e.g., butts into conversations/games)					
20. Often has difficulty sitting still, being quiet, or inhibiting impulses in the classroom or at home					
B - TOTAL SCORE (Hyperactivity)					

 Checklist continued on back.

Behavior Checklist

TOTAL FOCUS

For each item, check the column which best describes this child:	Not at All (0)	Just a Little (1)	Quite a Bit (2)	Very Much (3)	Score
21. Often has trouble taking no for an answer					
22. Often is excitable, impulsive					
23. Often cries easily					
24. Often loses temper					
25. Often blames others for his or her mistakes or misbehavior					
26. Often is restless or overactive					
27. Often disturbs other children					
28. Often changes mood quickly and drastically					
29. Often easily frustrated if demands are not met immediately					
30. Often is negative, defiant, disobedient, or hostile toward authority figures					
C - TOTAL SCORE (Behavior/Self-Control)					
31. Has difficulty getting started on classroom assignments					
32. Has difficulty staying on task for an entire classroom period					
33. Has problems in completion of work on classroom assignments					
34. Has problems in accuracy or neatness of written work in the classroom					
35. Has difficulty attending to a group classroom activity or discussion					
36. Has difficulty making transitions to the next topic or classroom period					
37. Has problems in interactions with peers in the classroom					
38. Has problems in interactions with staff (teacher or aide)					
39. Has difficulty remaining quiet according to classroom rules					
40. Has difficulty staying seated according to classroom rules					
D - TOTAL SCORE (Academic Achievement/School)					
OVERALL TOTAL SCORE (A+B+C+D)					

TOTAL FOCUS Behavior Checklist

For each item, check the column which best describes this child:	Not at All (0)	Just a Little (1)	Quite a Bit (2)	Very Much (3)	Score
1. Often fails to give close attention to details or makes careless mistakes in schoolwork or tasks					
2. Often has difficulty sustaining attention in tasks or play activities					
3. Often does not seem to listen when spoken to directly					
4. Often does not follow through on instructions and fails to finish schoolwork, chores, or duties					
5. Often has difficulty organizing tasks and activities					
6. Often avoids, dislikes, or reluctantly engages in tasks requiring sustained mental effort					
7. Often loses things necessary for activities (e.g., toys, school assignments, pencils, or books)					
8. Often is distracted by outside stimuli					
9. Often is forgetful in daily activities					
10. Often has difficulty maintaining alertness, orienting to requests, or executing directions					
A - TOTAL SCORE (Attention/Concentration)					
11. Often fidgets with hands or feet or squirms in seat					
12. Often leaves seat in classroom or in other situations in which remaining seated is expected					
13. Often runs about or climbs excessively in situations in which remaining seated is expected					
14. Often has difficulty playing or engaging in leisure activities quietly					
15. Often is "on the go" or often acts as if "driven by a motor"					
16. Often talks excessively					
17. Often blurts out answers before questions have been completed					
18. Often has difficulty awaiting turn					
19. Often interrupts or intrudes on others (e.g., butts into conversations/games)					
20. Often has difficulty sitting still, being quiet, or inhibiting impulses in the classroom or at home					
B - TOTAL SCORE (Hyperactivity)					

 Checklist continued on back.

TOTAL FOCUS Behavior Checklist

For each item, check the column which best describes this child:	Not at All (0)	Just a Little (1)	Quite a Bit (2)	Very Much (3)	Score
21. Often has trouble taking no for an answer					
22. Often is excitable, impulsive					
23. Often cries easily					
24. Often loses temper					
25. Often blames others for his or her mistakes or misbehavior					
26. Often is restless or overactive					
27. Often disturbs other children					
28. Often changes mood quickly and drastically					
29. Often easily frustrated if demands are not met immediately					
30. Often is negative, defiant, disobedient, or hostile toward authority figures					
C - TOTAL SCORE (Behavior/Self-Control)					
31. Has difficulty getting started on classroom assignments					
32. Has difficulty staying on task for an entire classroom period					
33. Has problems in completion of work on classroom assignments					
34. Has problems in accuracy or neatness of written work in the classroom					
35. Has difficulty attending to a group classroom activity or discussion					
36. Has difficulty making transitions to the next topic or classroom period					
37. Has problems in interactions with peers in the classroom					
38. Has problems in interactions with staff (teacher or aide)					
39. Has difficulty remaining quiet according to classroom rules					
40. Has difficulty staying seated according to classroom rules					
D - TOTAL SCORE (Academic Achievement/School)					
OVERALL TOTAL SCORE (A+B+C+D)					

TOTAL FOCUS **Behavior Checklist**

For each item, check the column which best describes this child:	Not at All (0)	Just a Little (1)	Quite a Bit (2)	Very Much (3)	Score
1. Often fails to give close attention to details or makes careless mistakes in schoolwork or tasks					
2. Often has difficulty sustaining attention in tasks or play activities					
3. Often does not seem to listen when spoken to directly					
4. Often does not follow through on instructions and fails to finish schoolwork, chores, or duties					
5. Often has difficulty organizing tasks and activities					
6. Often avoids, dislikes, or reluctantly engages in tasks requiring sustained mental effort					
7. Often loses things necessary for activities (e.g., toys, school assignments, pencils, or books)					
8. Often is distracted by outside stimuli					
9. Often is forgetful in daily activities					
10. Often has difficulty maintaining alertness, orienting to requests, or executing directions					
A - TOTAL SCORE (Attention/Concentration)					
11. Often fidgets with hands or feet or squirms in seat					
12. Often leaves seat in classroom or in other situations in which remaining seated is expected					
13. Often runs about or climbs excessively in situations in which remaining seated is expected					
14. Often has difficulty playing or engaging in leisure activities quietly					
15. Often is "on the go" or often acts as if "driven by a motor"					
16. Often talks excessively					
17. Often blurts out answers before questions have been completed					
18. Often has difficulty awaiting turn					
19. Often interrupts or intrudes on others (e.g., butts into conversations/games)					
20. Often has difficulty sitting still, being quiet, or inhibiting impulses in the classroom or at home					
B - TOTAL SCORE (Hyperactivity)					

 Checklist continued on back.

TOTAL FOCUS Behavior Checklist

For each item, check the column which best describes this child:	Not at All (0)	Just a Little (1)	Quite a Bit (2)	Very Much (3)	Score
21. Often has trouble taking no for an answer					
22. Often is excitable, impulsive					
23. Often cries easily					
24. Often loses temper					
25. Often blames others for his or her mistakes or misbehavior					
26. Often is restless or overactive					
27. Often disturbs other children					
28. Often changes mood quickly and drastically					
29. Often easily frustrated if demands are not met immediately					
30. Often is negative, defiant, disobedient, or hostile toward authority figures					
C - TOTAL SCORE (Behavior/Self-Control)					
31. Has difficulty getting started on classroom assignments					
32. Has difficulty staying on task for an entire classroom period					
33. Has problems in completion of work on classroom assignments					
34. Has problems in accuracy or neatness of written work in the classroom					
35. Has difficulty attending to a group classroom activity or discussion					
36. Has difficulty making transitions to the next topic or classroom period					
37. Has problems in interactions with peers in the classroom					
38. Has problems in interactions with staff (teacher or aide)					
39. Has difficulty remaining quiet according to classroom rules					
40. Has difficulty staying seated according to classroom rules					
D - TOTAL SCORE (Academic Achievement/School)					
OVERALL TOTAL SCORE (A+B+C+D)					

Going to the park	Playing with friends	Getting into bed with parents
Making mud pies	Listening to a bedtime story	Playing on a swing set
Spending the night with friends or grandparents	Being lifted into the air	Feeding a pet
Rocking	Playing games	Making noises with rattles, pans or bells
Having a horsey ride (swinging on parent's foot)	Doing a puppet play	Having parents take a picture of the child
Talking into a sound recorder	Going out for hamburgers or pizza	Wearing dress-up clothes
Playing with clay or Play-Doh	Going someplace alone or with mom and dad	Helping plan the day's activities
Helping mom or dad	Having a longer time in the bathtub	Riding on a bicycle with mom or dad
Whirling in a circle by arms	Watching a rainstorm	Playing in the sandbox
Sitting in the chair with dad or mom	Going to the library	Going for a picnic
Bouncing on the bed	Playing outside	Riding a tricycle
Staying up late	Going on a trip to the zoo	Getting a piggy-back ride
Having a bubble bath	Singing songs	Skipping
Delaying a nap	Playing with stickers	Riding on dad's shoulders
Going outside at night	Having a family night	Helping to hold baby sister or brother
Swimming	Reading a story	Mixing cookie dough
Having a special dessert	Chewing gum	Finger painting
Drawing with crayons	Listening to the CD Player	Playing a game with parent(s)
Going to a museum	Playing a video game	Watching a video
Renting a video game	Renting a DVD	Computer time

Taking a trip to the park	Playing with friends	Having a bedtime story
Playing on the swing set	Spending the night with friends or grandparents	Going to a ball game
Eating out	Going someplace alone with dad or mom	Baking something in the kitchen
Planning a day's activities	Riding on a bicycle	Going on a fishing trip with dad or mom
Choosing a TV program	Taking time off from chores	Holding hands while walking
Using a cell phone	Dressing up in parent's clothes	Setting the table
Camping in the backyard	Going to the library	Chewing gum
Telling a round-robin story	Decorating the home for the holidays	Helping to make Jell-O, popcorn, or something similar
Helping to take a gift to a friend	Feeding the baby	Staying up late
Going to the movies, especially with a friend	Taking a trip with a friend	Playing a favorite CD
Coloring	Riding next to the window in the car	Going to a museum
Listening to themselves on a recording	Choosing the menu for a meal	Calling grandma to tell of their successes
Getting a promise to ride the escalator a few times in a store	Putting up schoolwork on the refrigerator door	Buying something
Planting a garden	Going for a picnic	Going skating, swimming or bowling
Making something, like a special craft with mom or dad	Ordering pizza	Going for a hike
Going canoeing, camping, fishing or skiing	Sleeping in a different place in the house	Doing a jigsaw puzzle
Decorating their own room	Having a special after-school snack	Having a special treat in their school lunch
Choosing a special breakfast	Playing a game with mom or dad like checkers, marbles or cards	Listening to the radio
Computer time	Playing a video game	Renting a video game
Watching a video	Renting a video	Skate boarding

HOME REWARD POSSIBILITIES FOR TEENAGERS		
Having dating privileges	Participating in activities w/friends	Having friends over
Taking dancing or music lessons	Redecorating their own room	Skating or bowling with friends
Additional texting or cell phone time	Using the iPod	Making a trip alone
Finding a part-time job	Taking the car to school for a day	Getting to stay out late
Having car privileges	Staying up late	Staying overnight with friends
Taking time off from chores	Having a date during the week	Getting a chance to earn money
Selecting TV programs	Being the chairman at a family meeting	A credit in their iTunes account
Getting a driver's license	Driving the car on a family trip	Camping out
Going to summer camp	Getting a special haircut/style	Going to an amusement park
Sitting at a separate table when the family eats out	Inviting a friend to eat out	Getting to sleep in late on the weekend
Having their own checking account	Receiving a magazine subscription	Working on a car or bike with friends
Buying a CD or downloading songs	Buying a new cell phone	Selecting something special for dinner
Going to the library	Going to the mall with friends	Going horseback riding
Going to a concert with friends	Going to the movies with friends	Computer time

A Warm Fuzzy Tale

by Claude M. Steiner

Once upon a time, a long time ago, there lived two happy people called Tim and Maggie with their two children, John and Lucy. To understand how happy they were you have to understand how things were in those days.

You see in those happy days everyone was given a small, soft Fuzzy Bag when born. Any time a person reached into this bag, they were able to pull out a Warm Fuzzy. Warm Fuzzies were very much in demand because whenever someone was given a Warm Fuzzy, it made them feel warm and fuzzy all over.

In those days it was very easy to get Warm Fuzzies. Anytime that somebody felt like it, he might walk up to you and say, "I'd like to have a Warm Fuzzy." You would then reach into your bag and pull out a Fuzzy the size of a child's hand. As soon as the Fuzzy saw the light of day it would smile and blossom into a large, shaggy, Warm Fuzzy. When you laid the Warm Fuzzy on the person's head, shoulder or lap it would snuggle up and melt right against their skin and make them feel good all over.

People were always asking each other for Warm Fuzzies, and since they were always given freely, getting enough of them was never a problem. There were always plenty to go around, and so everyone was happy and felt warm and fuzzy most of the time.

One day a bad witch who made salves and potions for sick people became angry because everyone was so happy and feeling good and no one was buying potions and salves. The witch was very clever and devised a very wicked plan. One beautiful morning while Maggie was playing with her daughter, the witch crept up to Tim, and whispered in his ear:

"See here, Tim, look at all the Fuzzies that Maggie is giving to Lucy. You know, if she keeps it up, she is going to run out and then there won't be any left for you!"

Tim was astonished. He turned to the witch and asked, "Do you mean to tell me that there isn't a Warm Fuzzy in our bag every time we reach into it?"

And the witch answered, "No, absolutely not, and once you run out, that's it. You don't have any more." With this the witch flew away on a broom, laughing and cackling all the way.

Tim took this to heart and began to notice every time Maggie gave away a Warm Fuzzy. He got very worried because he liked Maggie's Warm Fuzzies very much and did not want to give them up. He certainly did not think it was right for Maggie to be spending all her Warm Fuzzies on the children and other people.

Tim began to complain or sulk when he saw Maggie giving Warm Fuzzies to somebody else, and because Maggie loved him very much, she stopped giving Warm Fuzzies to other people as often, and reserved most of them for him.

The children watched this and soon began to get the idea that it was wrong to give Warm Fuzzies any time you were asked or felt like it. They too became very careful. They would watch their parents closely and whenever they felt that one of their parents was giving too many Fuzzies to others, they felt jealous and complained and sometimes even had a tantrum. And even though they found a Warm Fuzzy every time they reached into their bag, they began to feel guilty whenever they gave them away so they reached in less and less and became more and more stingy with them.

Before the witch, people used to gather in groups of three, four or five, never caring too much who was giving Warm Fuzzies to whom. After the coming of the witch, people began to pair off and to reserve all their Warm Fuzzies for each other, exclusively. When people forgot to be careful and gave a Warm Fuzzy to just anybody, they worried because they knew that somebody would probably resent sharing their Warm Fuzzies.

People began to give less and less Warm Fuzzies, and felt less warm and less fuzzy. They began to shrivel up and, occasionally, people would even die from lack of Warm Fuzzies. People felt worse and worse and, more and more, people went to the witch to buy potions and salves even though they didn't really seem to work.

Well, the situation was getting very serious indeed. The bad witch who had been watching all of this didn't really want the people to die (since dead people couldn't buy his salves and potions), so a new plan was devised.

Everyone was given, free of charge, a bag that was very similar to the Fuzzy Bag except that this one was cold while the Fuzzy Bag was warm. Inside of the witch's bag were Cold Pricklies. These Cold Pricklies did not make people feel warm and fuzzy; in fact they made them feel cold and prickly instead. But the Cold Pricklies were better than nothing and they did prevent people's backs from shriveling up.

So, from then on, when somebody asked for a Warm Fuzzy, people who were worried about depleting their supply would say, "I can't give you a Warm Fuzzy, but would you like a Cold Prickly instead?"

Sometimes, two people would walk up to each other, thinking that maybe they could get a Warm Fuzzy this time, but one of them would change his mind and they would wind up giving each other Cold Pricklies instead. So, the end result was that people were not dying anymore but a lot of people were very unhappy and feeling very cold and prickly indeed.

The situation got very complicated since the coming of the witch because there were fewer and fewer Warm Fuzzies around and Warm Fuzzies, which used to be free as air, became extremely valuable.

This caused people to do all sorts of things in order to get Warm Fuzzies. People who could not find a generous partner had to buy their Warm Fuzzies and had to work long hours to earn the money. These fake Warm Fuzzies were really Plastic Fuzzies, and they caused additional problems.

For instance, two or more people would get together and freely give each other Plastic Fuzzies. They expected to feel good, but they came away feeling bad instead. People got very confused never realizing that their cold, prickly feelings were because they had been given a lot of Plastic Fuzzies.

So the situation was very, very dismal and it all started because of the coming of the witch who made people believe that some day, when least expected, they might reach into their Warm Fuzzy Bag and find no more.

Not long ago, a young woman with big hips came to this unhappy land. She seemed not to have heard about the bad witch and was not worried about running out of Warm Fuzzies. She gave them out freely, even when not asked. They called her the Hip Woman and disapproved of her because she was giving the children the idea that they should not worry about running out of Warm Fuzzies. The children liked her very much because they felt good around her and they began to follow her example giving out Warm Fuzzies whenever they felt like it.

This made the grownups very worried. To protect the children from depleting their supplies of Warm Fuzzies they passed a law. The law made it a criminal offense to give out Warm Fuzzies in a reckless manner or without a license. Many children, however, seemed not to care; and in spite of the law they continued to give each other Warm Fuzzies whenever they felt like it and always when asked. Because there were many, many children, almost as many as grown ups, it began to look as if maybe they would have their way.

As of now its hard to say what will happen. Will the grownups' laws stop the recklessness of the children?

Are the grownups going to join with the Hip Woman and the children in taking a chance that there will always be as many Warm Fuzzies as needed?

Will they remember the days their children are trying to bring back when Warm Fuzzies were abundant because people gave them away freely ?

The struggle spread all over the land and is probably going on right were you live. If you want to, and I hope you do, you can join by freely giving and asking for Warm Fuzzies and being as loving and healthy as you can.